Hero...

Here are tales of magi...
mysterious prophecies, o...
journeys t...
The myths and legends of ... ... Greek civilisation are
among the best stories ever told, and have become an
inseparable part of our literature and culture. James Reeves,
himself a distinguished author and poet, made his own
selection from these heroic tales and retells them for today's
young readers.

Heroes and Monsters, includes the adventures of Jason and the
Argonauts in their quest for the Golden Fleece, Perseus
setting out to slay the gorgon Medusa, the twelve labours of
Hercules, the story of Theseus defying the monstrous
Minotaur in the Labyrinth of Crete, Orpheus braving the
powers of the Underworld to win back his lost bride, the Fall
of Troy, and the voyages of Odysseus.

'An excellent new rendering of those beautiful, barbarous
(sometimes), but oddly essential myths . . . Anyone seeking a
modern version need look no further than this.'

Naomi Lewis, *The Observer*

Heroes and Monsters

*Legends of Ancient Greece
retold by*
JAMES REEVES

Illustrated by Sara Silcock

PIPER BOOKS

First published 1969 by Blackie and Son Ltd
Published in Piccolo 1987 by Pan Books Ltd,
This Piper edition published 1989 by Pan Books Ltd,
Cavaye Place, London SW10 9PG
Text copyright © by the Estate of James Reeves 1969, 1987
9 8 7 6 5
ISBN 0 330 29707 4
Photoset by Parker Typesetting Service, Leicester
Printed in England by Clays Ltd, St Ives plc

Contents

		PAGE
	Introduction	7
	Pronunciation Guide	11
1	The Beginnings of Man: *Prometheus and Pandora*	17
2	Winter and Summer: *Demeter and Persephone*	21
3	Daedalus and Icarus	28
4	Phaeton's Journey	33
5	King Midas	
	1 The Golden Touch	41
	2 A Pair of Ass's Ears	46
6	Jason and the Argonauts	
	1 The Boyhood of Jason	50
	2 Voyage of the Argo	56
	3 The Golden Fleece	65
7	The Labours of Heracles	73
8	Apollo and Daphne	91
9	The Gorgon's Head	
	1 Perseus and Danaë	96
	2 The Slaying of Medusa	101
	3 The Giant Atlas	107
	4 Perseus and Andromeda	111
	5 The Return of Perseus	116
10	Philemon and Baucis	120
11	Eros and Psyche	125

12 Ceyx and Alcyone   140
13 Orpheus and Eurydice   146
14 Theseus and the Minotaur
     1 *The Journey to Athens*   155
     2 *The Minotaur*   164
15 Arion   171
16 The Fall of Troy   178
17 Odysseus and Polyphemus   185
18 Odysseus and Circe   192
19 Scylla and Charybdis   202
20 The Homecoming of Odysseus   210

Introduction

In this book you will read some of the world's greatest folk tales. A folk tale is one which has come down to us from the lips of the 'folk' – that is, the common people of any land; it is anonymous – it has, that is to say, no known original author, whoever may have chosen to write it down later; it is also widespread, appearing in different forms in different countries. The folk tales of Ancient Greece – some of them older than the work of one of the greatest of all poets, Homer, who is thought to have lived about a thousand years before Christianity – are among those which have charmed and delighted people for many centuries, because of their variety, their magic, their vigour, their excitement and their poetic treatment of man and nature.

Now the Greeks have always been noted for their enquiring minds. They had the virtue of curiosity, which, as Dr Johnson said, 'is, in great and generous minds, the first passion and the last'. Had it not been for the enquiring mind of Greece, western Europe would have known little progress, and we should have been without some of our finest stories, our greatest plays and our most beautiful poetry. These ancient Greeks looked at the world around them and wondered how it came to be as it is. They gradually invented and passed on to their children a vast body of tradition about the nature of men, women and animals, about the beginnings of the natural world and the monsters that inhabited it, and, above all, about the gods who ruled the world of men. The gods were all-important to the Greeks. Invisibly they reigned in the upper air or on mountain tops, especially that of Mount Olympus, coming down to earth sometimes in disguise to alter or supervise the lives of men. The idea of one god only is a Jewish and, later, a Christian one. The Greeks had many gods, each responsible for a different part of the earth or a different department in human affairs. The belief in the existence of these gods explained the facts of nature as they presented themselves to the imagination of the Greeks. Thus Zeus, the chief of all the gods, was the cause of thunder and lightning. Poseidon ruled the seas, and Hades, or Dis, the underworld, to which all must go when they die. The troubles of men arose from one of two causes: either they did wrong and angered the gods, or the gods quarrelled among themselves, and their quarrels were reflected in war or famine or some other disaster on earth. In the same way, happiness and good fortune came to men because the gods were pleased and willed it so.

The gods had the same passions and weaknesses as men. Because of the Sun god Apollo's desire to possess the maiden Daphne, who did not love him, she ran from him and escaped him, just as he was catching up with her, by turning into a laurel tree. This tale charmingly and satisfyingly explained the origin of one of the trees found growing in the land of the Greeks. What was the beginning of those faults and weaknesses of men – anger, greed, jealousy, spite, cruelty and the rest – by which so much trouble and misery is caused? The Greeks had the delightful idea that at some former time – a lost golden age – all these things were shut up in a box, which it was forbidden to open; but Pandora, carried away by her foolish inquisitiveness, in reckless disobedience lifted the lid. Instantly all the evils in the box escaped and have never been recaptured since. We may smile at some of these folk tales, but we must admire their combination of simplicity and ingenuity.

Not all the legends of the Greeks were about nature or the quarrels and loves of the gods. Some of the best were about ancient heroes, such as Perseus or Jason or Heracles. Their heroic deeds were recounted in songs and stories, growing and changing as they were handed down, age after age. These heroes, or demigods, probably had historical originals, though many miraculous and superhuman actions were woven into their legends, so that we can no longer say what was true and what was invented.

It would take too long to describe here the world of the Greeks and their marvellous tales. The stories can be enjoyed for themselves, without the scholar's knowledge of their meaning and origins. But some readers may wonder how they came down to us. They came first from the ancient Greek poets, Homer and Hesiod, from later poets such as Pindar, and from scholars and collectors such as Diodorus. One very important source is the writings of the Roman poet Ovid, and it is from his poems that many of our later versions come. The Romans had no true mythology themselves, only a rather vague worship of the spirits of nature, of agriculture and husbandry. But when they conquered Greece, they were as delighted with the folklore they found as anyone has been later. They took over the Greek gods and worshipped them under names of their own; thus the Greek goddess of love, Aphrodite, became Venus; the leader of the gods, Zeus, became Jupiter or Jove; the hero Heracles was known to the Romans as Hercules. Through the Romans, then, much that

9

might have been lost of Greek mythology has survived, to entertain and astonish readers in all lands for the past two thousand years.

One other feature of this book remains to be mentioned. English readers, since the days when Greek used to be taught in most schools, find difficulty in pronouncing the names of Greek gods, heroes or places. A guide to the pronunciation of these names is given at the beginning of this book, and where the Romans had different forms of these names, these are also given. This guide is worth studying, for it will surely be agreed that the stories sound better if Penelope, Persephone or Telemachus are read as they should be and not turned into English-sounding names.

J.R.
Lewes, 1969

Pronunciation Guide

Roman equivalents of Greek names are given in brackets.
AE = EE (as in KEEP); CH = K; PH = F
C is hard (as in CAT) except where marked thus: AÇIS
Ȳ long (as in SKY); Ў short (as in MYTH)
Other vowels short unless marked thus: ACHILLĒS

Abdē'ra
Absyr'tus
Achi'llés
Ā'çis
Acri'sius
Admē'tus
Aeāē'a
Aegē'an
Ae'gēūs
Ae'olus
Ae'son
Aë'tēs
Ae'thra
Alçi'nous
Alcmē'né
Alçȳ'onē
Alphē'us

A'mўcus
A'mўmō'nē
Androm'eda
Anti'nous
Aphrodī'tē (Venus)
Apo'llō
Ā'rēs (Mars)
Arethū'sa
Ar'gonauts
Aria'dne
Ari'on
Art'emis (Diana)
Asclē'pius
Atalan'ta
Ath'amas
Athē'nē (Minerva)
Augē'as

Auto'lўcus

Bria'reus

Ca'lāis
Callī'ope
Calў'pso
Cassiopē'ia
Çer'berus
Çē'ўx
Chā'ron
Charўb'dis
Chī'os
Chī'ron
Çir'çē
Clēō'nae
Clў'menē
Cno'ssos
Col'chis
Çўclō'pes

Dae'dalus
Dan'ae
Daph'ne
Del'phi
Dēmē'ter (Ceres)
Dic'tўs
Diomē'dēs
Dionў'sus (Bacchus)
Drў'ads

Ē'lis
Encel'adus
Epidau'rus
Epimē'theus

Eri'danus
Ē'ros (Cupid)
Ery'theia
Eumāē'us
Euryclei'a
Euryd'içē
Euryl'ochus
Eurym'achus
Eurў'sthēūs
Eurў'tion

Galatē'a
Ge'rўon

Hā'dēs (Pluto)
Hec'atē
Hec'tor
Helī'adēs
Hel'icon
Hē'lios
Hel'lē
Hēl'lespont
Hēphae'stus
Hē'ra (Juno)
He'raclēs (Hercules)
Her'mēs
Hespe'ridēs
Hes'perus
Hippodamī'a
Hippol'ўta
Hў'dra
Hў'las
Hў'men
Hўperbor'eans

12

I'carus

Iolā'us

Iol'cos

Iō'nia

I'ris

I'thaca

Ixī'on

Lā'dōn

Lāer'tēs

Laestrȳ'gonians

Lāo'cǒon

Laris'sa

Lȳ'dia

Lȳn'cēus

Mēdē'a

Medū'sa

Meg'ara

Melan'thius

Menelā'us

Mī'das

Mī'nos

Mī'notaur

Mor'phēus

Mycē'nae

Nausicā'a

Nemē'a

Nephē'le

Nē'reïds

Nē'rēus

Odȳ'ssēus (Ulysses)

Olȳm'pus

Or'phēus

Pactō'lus

Pallā'dium

Pandor'a

Parnas'sus

Pasi'phaē

Peg'asus

Pe'lias

Penel'opē

Pēnē'us

Per'dix

Perian'der

Perse'phonē

Per'sēus

Phaeā'cians

Phā'eton

Philē'mon

Phī'nēus

Phrix'us

Phrȳ'gia

Polȳdec'tēs

Polȳdēū'cēs (Pollux)

Polȳphē'mus

Posei'don (Neptune)

Prī'am

Procrus'tēs

Promē'thēus

Psȳ'chē

Sche'ria

Scī'ron

Scȳl'la

Se'riphos

Sīlē'nus

Si'nis

Sī'non

Si'sўphus

Stўgian

Stўmphā'lus

Stўx

Sўmplē'gadēs

Sў'rinx

Tan'talus

Tele'machus

Ten'edos

Thēb(e)s

Thē'sēūs

Thes'salў

Ti'rўns

Tī'tans

Tmō'lus

Troi'zen

Tў'phōn (Typhoeus)

Zeph'ўrus

Zē'tēs

Zeūs (Jupiter *or* Jove)

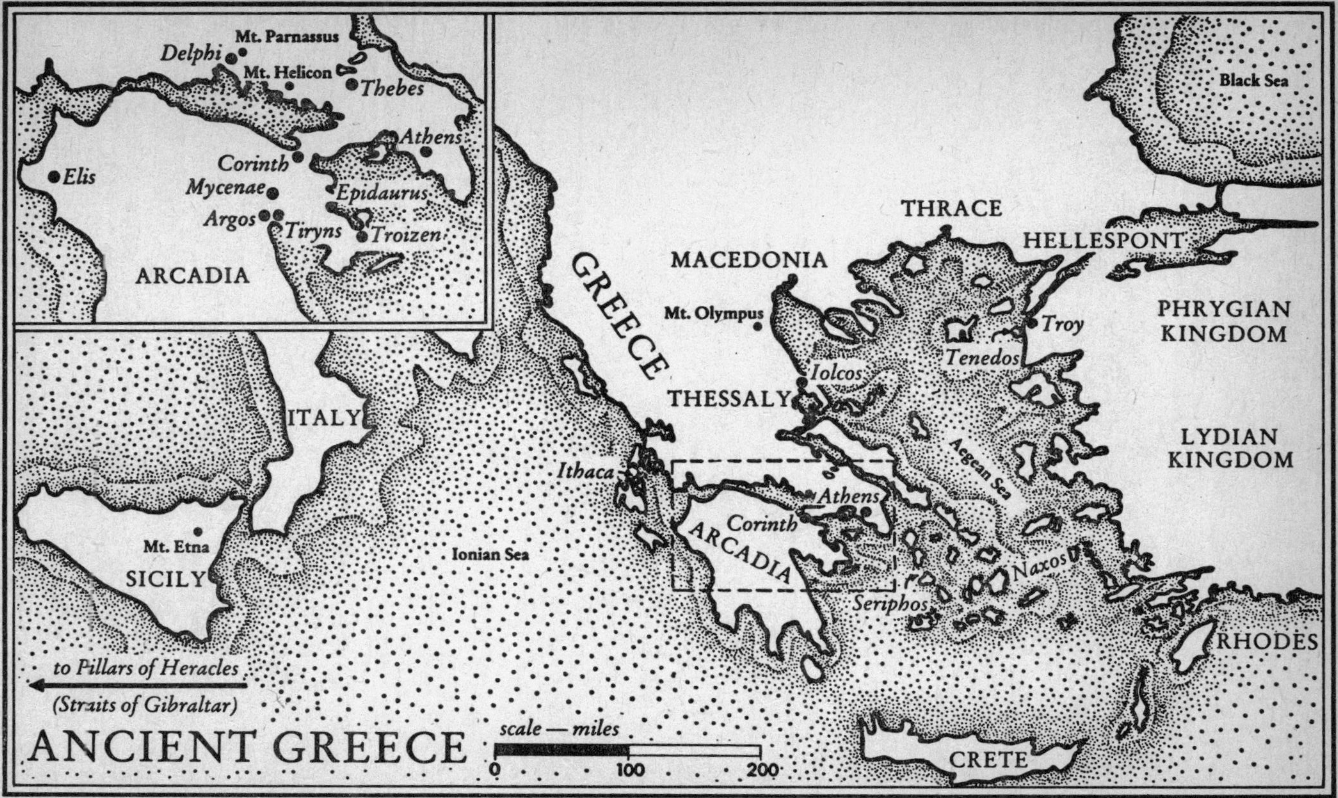
ANCIENT GREECE
Mt. Parnassus
Delphi
Mt. Helicon
Thebes
Athens
Corinth
Elis
Mycenae
Epidaurus
Argos
Tiryns
Troizen
ARCADIA
Black Sea
THRACE
HELLESPONT
MACEDONIA
GREECE
Mt. Olympus
Troy
PHRYGIAN KINGDOM
Tenedos
Iolcos
THESSALY
ITALY
LYDIAN KINGDOM
Aegean Sea
Ithaca
Athens
Corinth
ARCADIA
Mt. Etna
Ionian Sea
SICILY
Naxos
Seriphos
RHODES
to Pillars of Heracles
(Straits of Gibraltar)
scale — miles
0
100
200
CRETE

1

The Beginnings of Man:
Prometheus and Pandora

WHAT were things like in the very beginning? This is a question which has puzzled men of all times and places. None knows the answer for certain, because the records of history do not go back far enough. Like other races, the Greeks asked themselves the question, and the answer they gave was this.

In the beginning of time, before the creation of heaven, earth and ocean, there was chaos – vague and dark, neither liquid, solid nor vapour, but a mixture of all three. Everything was a shapeless mass, in which lay hid the seeds of things as they were later to be. At last the oldest of the gods brought order into chaos and separated heaven from earth and earth from sea. The heavens were clear and filled with innumerable stars; the earth was dry and contained hills, valleys and plains; the sea flowed blue and green in its restless currents about the shores of the world. Of all the elements that made up chaos, fire was the lightest, and so fire rose up highest and formed the heavens. Earth sank down, and ocean remained below, bearing up the earth.

The earth began to put forth trees and grass, and in these the creatures of nature ran and climbed. Fishes swam in the fresh rivers that flowed down the valleys; other kinds of fish inhabited the ocean. So things began after the creation of heaven, earth and sea.

Then one of the gods – it is not known which – thought that a nobler creature was wanted than all the animals of the air, the land and the water – some creature wiser and greater than they. So man was made. The creator of man was the giant Prometheus. He came of the race of the Titans, a giant people who were born on the earth before man. Prometheus saw that man must be made from the earth, since only gods could be made of heavenly substance. He took handfuls of earth and kneaded them with water into the shape of a god. What separated man from all other animals was that, while they crept on their bellies or ran and trotted about on all fours, man alone walked upright on two feet. While other creatures looked downwards towards the earth from which they came, man looked upwards to the heavens, because he had been made in the image of the gods who dwell there.

It was to Prometheus the Titan and his brother Epimetheus that the gods entrusted the work of making man and fitting him to live on earth among the animals. It was the special task of Epimetheus to provide the creatures with the qualities and parts they needed – swiftness to the tiger, strength to the lion, wings for the birds and fins for the fishes; the fox was given cunning, the wolf ferocity and the elephant his huge size and his thick, leathery skin.

But what was to be given to man, who was to be greater than all other animals? He could never have claws like those of the tiger, nor speed like that of the horse; he could not fly like an eagle or grow horns like a deer. Even the little hare was faster than he, and the spotted leopard better at hiding himself among the trees. How could man live in a world full of creatures such as these? His skin was fine and soft, his teeth and nails small, his whole body unfitted to survive without some greater power. The truth was that Epimetheus had used up all the gifts in his possession and had nothing special left to give to man. So he went to his brother Prometheus and asked him to help.

'What can I give man,' he asked, 'to make him stronger and greater than all other creatures?'

'We must give him something from heaven,' answered Prometheus, 'something beyond the power of all others upon earth.'

Accordingly Prometheus went up to heaven with a torch in his hand and stole fire from the sun. For fire is of all things that which truly belongs to heaven. So man was given the heavenly gift of fire, and with this he gained the mastery over all other creatures on earth. With fire man was able to make tools to cultivate the earth. He had no long nails to scratch in the soil so that he could sow seeds, but with the spade and the plough he was able to do so. He was able, with the help of fire, to make sharp weapons to subdue the creatures around him; he could make scythes to cut the grass of the field and so keep alive the cattle on which he fed and the horses on which he went hunting. With fire he could warm himself and his home, so that he could live in places that would otherwise have been too cold. With fire he was able to melt down metals to make images and statues, coins and ornaments. So fire, the gift of Prometheus, gave man the mastery over all nature and enabled him to become strong and powerful beyond the strength of his own body.

Till now, so the Greeks believed, no woman had been made. At length Zeus determined that man needed a companion and a helpmate. Some believed that woman was sent, not as a friend to man, but to plague him for having taken the gift of fire which Prometheus had stolen from heaven. Whatever was in the mind of Zeus, chief of the gods, he sent Pandora to be the first woman on earth. She was made, not on the earth like man, but in heaven. Every god gave her some special gift.

Aphrodite gave her beauty, Hera, the wife of Zeus, gave her womanliness, Athene wisdom, Apollo the gift of a musical voice. So Pandora came down from heaven to live on earth in the house of the Titan Epimetheus.

Now Epimetheus had in his house a huge box containing many things he had had no use for when he placed man upon earth. These were all manner of troubles – diseases and plagues; aches and pains; disorders of the mind; worry, fear, envy, jealousy and greed. Since all these things were firmly shut in the box, man had so far no experience of them. He could not even guess what they were.

'On no account,' said Epimetheus to Pandora sternly, 'are you to try to open this box and find out what is inside. Remember what I say, and leave the box alone.'

For a long time Pandora did as she was told. Yet all the time she longed to know what was in the box. Had she not been given the gift of curiosity? In the end she was unable to resist temptation. One day, when Epimetheus was away from home, curiosity got the better of patience, and she worked the lid from the box. As it slid to the ground, she bent down and looked in. At once she was surrounded by all the ills on earth – cramp and toothache for the body, spite and envy for the mind. All these evils, and many more besides, rose from the box and whirled past poor Pandora's head, scattering themselves over the face of the earth.

At once Pandora, seeing what she had done and how foolish it was to disobey the Titan's command, picked up the lid of the box with trembling hands and tried to cram it on. It was too late. All the evils contained in the box had escaped, all but one thing, and that is not an evil but a blessing. It was hope. That alone remained as woman's gift to man. That alone was left him as a comfort when he is surrounded by disease and wickedness.

Winter and Summer:
Demeter and Persephone

THE goddess Demeter lived in the island of Sicily in the middle of the Mediterranean Sea. She was the goddess of Nature, and in her protection were the fields and meadows, the flowers and herbs, corn, figs and olives – everything that grows in the earth and nourishes life. So it was not surprising that her home should be in Sicily, for this is the land of sunshine and plenty. In those far-off times there was no winter, only everlasting summer, so there were always flowers to gather and fruits to eat; the trees were covered with

green leaves the whole year through, and among them the birds nested and sang in endless delight.

Demeter had one daughter, of whom she was very fond – the beautiful Persephone. It was the girl's greatest pleasure to go with her friends, young maidens like herself, into the fields to gather flowers. This she would do every day, returning home at night to her mother.

Then one day Persephone did not come home. Towards evening the girl's friends came running to Demeter to tell her they had lost Persephone in the fields of Enna, a beautiful valley in the middle of Sicily, where the flowers were especially lovely. It was one of their favourite places. They often went there, and Persephone well knew the way home. But she had strayed away from her friends, so that they could not find her anywhere. They ran here and there calling her name, but the only answer that came to them was the bleating of sheep and the notes of the birds in the trees.

At once Demeter set out to look for her daughter.

Now what had happened was this. Many years before, a race of giants, of whom the chief were Enceladus, Briareus and Typhon, had made war against the gods. The gods were victorious, and for punishment they shut the giants up under the earth. So great were their groans and rumblings, so hot and fiery their breath, that a mighty volcano was formed, by name Etna, at one end of the island of Sicily. Through the hole in this mountain came the roaring of the imprisoned giants and their fiery breath. Whenever the giants were especially angry, the volcano erupted in great flames and clouds of black, evil-smelling smoke.

Hades, god of the underworld, became alarmed at this. He ruled over the gloomy kingdom of the dead, known sometimes also as Hades, sometimes as the underworld. He was afraid that the giants would crack open the surface of the earth and let rain and storms, wind and sunshine into his kingdom. So he decided to travel up to the earth to see that everything was safe and sound, and that there was no danger of the earth being broken open.

Hades mounted his black chariot drawn by four coal-black horses and drove it about the earth – as strange a sight as had ever been seen in the fair land of Sicily.

It so happened that his eyes fell upon the lovely Persephone, just as she had strayed from her maidens in the valley of Enna, to gather flowers of especial beauty and freshness. Seeing her with her arms full of flowers, Hades' heart was touched, and he felt the loneliness of his position as king of the underworld with no queen to reign beside him. Stern and gloomy though he was, his features softened and his eyes were filled with longing. Persephone looked up as a great shadow fell upon her, the shadow of a black coach drawn by four coal-black steeds.

Hades swiftly reined in his horses at the girl's side, stooped down and seized her, lifting her up into the chariot beside him.

'For long years,' he said, 'I have been looking for a queen. It is you I have chosen. I can see that you were sent by my brother Zeus to be my bride.'

Half fascinated, half fearful, Persephone gazed up at the dark and gloomy king who had taken her into his chariot. Her armful of flowers fell to the ground. But already the horses were moving swiftly away from the valley where Persephone had left her friends. She could not escape. Besides, her heart was moved to pity by the sight of the stern and lonely god who stood beside her, handling the horses' reins.

They came to a stream named Cyane, too broad and deep for the chariot to pass. Immediately Hades raised his whip and struck the bank of the river. A great cleft at once opened in the ground, and horses and chariot plunged into the depths of the earth. So Persephone went down into Hades, there to reign as queen at the side of her husband and master.

For many days Demeter wandered over the whole earth, searching for her lost daughter. She asked everyone she met if they had seen her, but no one could tell her anything. At last she returned to her native Sicily, but she cared no more for the beauty of the earth. In anger she laid a curse upon it, so that all the green things began to wither; mildew attacked the crops; disease struck the sheep and cattle. Fruits shrivelled and flowers withered on their stems; biting winds froze the streams, and the leaves turned brown and fell from the trees. It seemed as if the whole of Nature would die, and men and women began to perish for lack of food. All over the earth people offered sacrifices to the gods, for they saw that some terrible evil had befallen them. It was the first winter but they did not know it. They begged the gods to have pity on their plight and to forgive whatever crimes they had committed.

One day Demeter stood by the fountain Arethusa, and the fountain began to plead with her to have pity on the earth.

'Perhaps I can tell you something of Persephone,' she said. 'When I lived in Greece, I was a maiden, but one day when I was bathing in the River Alpheus, the river god pursued me. I prayed to the goddess Artemis to protect me, and she turned me into a stream. Still the river god Alpheus chased me, wishing to mix his waters with mine, so Artemis opened a hole in the earth, and down this I flowed. Here in Sicily I rose once more to the surface of the earth, where I am the fountain you now see.'

'What has this to do with my lost daughter?' Demeter asked angrily.

'In my passage through the underworld,' Arethusa went on, 'I saw Persephone.'

'You saw her?' cried Demeter. 'Was she alive or dead?'

'She was alive. She looked sad, as if she missed the flowers and the meadows, for the underworld is grey and desolate. Yet there was something queenly about her, as if she had become a ruler in the kingdom of death. I think Hades has taken her to be his queen.'

'Then she must come back!' said Demeter, and at once she drove her chariot towards Mount Olympus, the home of the gods.

Here there was a considerable stir, for Zeus, chief of the gods, was beset by prayers of men and women all over the earth that their lands should again be made green and fruitful. He told Demeter of the people's prayers and asked her why she was no longer caring for the earth, as she used to.

'The fault is that of your brother Hades,' answered Demeter. 'He has stolen my daughter Persephone and taken her to live as his queen in the underworld. I must have her back. You must order your brother to restore her.'

Zeus did not want to offend so important a god as his brother Hades, and for a long time he argued with Demeter. But she told him that, unless Persephone was restored to her, she would never again make the earth fruitful, and the whole of humankind would perish. So at last Zeus agreed to order Hades to send Persephone back on one condition, namely, that during her stay she had eaten none of the food of the underworld.

Hermes, the winged messenger of the gods, was sent to Hades to demand the release of Persephone upon the condition named. Hades was bound to obey the chief of all the gods, and with much sorrow he bade farewell to his wife and told her to go with Hermes back to her mother. In some ways Persephone did not want to leave her stern and gloomy husband, and she had taken pity upon the dead who wandered sadly about the desolate ways of the underworld. But she missed the bright fields of home; so, half grieving, half glad, she prepared to go with Hermes. But another surprise was in store. A gardening boy named Ascalaphus came running to the king to tell him he had seen the queen eat the fruit of the pomegranate, which is the food of the dead.

'Seven seeds I saw her take,' he told Hades, who forthwith refused to release Persephone.

The messenger of the gods flew off to report what had happened, and Demeter was so enraged by the news that, in revenge, she turned the boy Ascalaphus into a screech-owl. To this day the bird has flown by night, visiting the haunts of the dead and terrifying men and women in their beds with the thought of death.

However, once more Demeter refused to restore the earth to its former fruitfulness. By now almost everything was withered; cattle were dying everywhere; men and women and children were starving. So it was necessary that something should be done immediately. Once more Hermes flew back and forth between Mount Olympus and the underworld until at last an agreement was reached. For half the year Persephone was to remain in the underworld with Hades; for the other half of the year she would live on earth with her mother, the goddess of Nature. With this arrangement poor Demeter was forced to be content. She would rather have had Persephone with her all the year round, but it had been decreed otherwise.

And this is how, the Greeks tell us, the seasons began. In spring Persephone comes from the gloomy underworld to live on earth; the birds sing, and the buds burst into flower, and the trees put on their green leaves. In autumn, after the harvests are gathered, she bids farewell to her mother and returns to the underworld to spend the winter with her husband Hades. Then the leaves of the fig-tree wither; the vine shrivels; cold winds come, bringing snow and hail. It seems as if the earth is dying and the sun will never shine again with all his old force and splendour. But spring and summer will come, and once more the fields will be glad with flowers and corn, as they were that first spring when Queen Persephone returned to sorrowing Demeter, mother of Nature and goddess of fruitfulness.

3

Daedalus and Icarus

OF all the Greeks, Daedalus, an Athenian, was most widely known, throughout the ancient world, as a cunning crafts-man, artist and inventor. He it was who perfected the art of sculpture. There had been statues before his time, but none had ever been so lifelike as those of Daedalus. They were famous not only in Greece but over the sea in Egypt and other parts of Africa. In Egypt he was worshipped as a god. But he was not simply a sculptor, he was also an inventor and an improver of all works useful to man. He built baths in Greece and a great reservoir in sun-baked Sicily. He con-structed the masts and yards of ships, while his son Icarus was thought to have been the inventor of sails.

One of the principal crafts invented by Daedalus was that of carpentry. He was said by ancient writers to have invented glue, the plumb-line, the gimlet, the axe and the saw. But some say it was his pupil Perdix who invented the saw, making the first examples from the backbones of big fish.

Daedalus had become very proud of his world-wide repu-tation as a sculptor and inventor, and he was glad to take as a pupil his sister's son, Perdix. But Perdix became so quick and clever a pupil that people began to say he was a better crafts-man than his master. This made Daedalus jealous. One day, in

rage and envy, he took the young man to the top of a high tower he had built in order, as he said, to show him the wonders of Athens. Then, when Perdix was gazing out towards the sea, Daedalus pushed him from the top of the tower, intending to kill him. But the young man was protected by the goddess Athene, who turned him into a partridge before he hit the ground. So by becoming a bird Perdix narrowly escaped death, and from that time to this the partridge has always flown low.

For this attempted murder Daedalus was condemned to death by the Athenian court of justice. No sooner had he heard his sentence than the famous craftsman fled the city and took refuge in the island of Crete. King Minos had already heard of Daedalus's great skill as an inventor, so he welcomed him into his service and made him construct many ingenious things at his palace of Cnossos.

Now the god Poseidon had sent a beautiful white bull to Crete with orders that it should be sacrificed to him there. But Minos's wife Pasiphae fell in love with the bull, and persuaded her husband not to sacrifice it. In revenge Poseidon caused Pasiphae to give birth to a monster with the head of a bull and the body of a man. This was the famous Minotaur, and it was such a cause of shame to King Minos that he determined to hide it. Accordingly he sent for Daedalus and made him construct a hiding-place in which the monster might live without being seen. Daedalus built a maze or labyrinth, in which a series of cunning passages led to the centre. So intricate was the labyrinth that Daedalus himself could scarcely find his way out to the entrance. Here the Minotaur was able to stamp about and charge angrily back and forth amidst the maze of alleyways unseen by anyone.

'This is indeed a marvellous construction,' said Minos, 'and it is easy to see that you are the cleverest designer the world has ever seen.'

So Minos kept Daedalus in Crete, making him construct other marvels of ingenuity – baths and fountains, temples and statues, paved floors and splendid flights of stairs.

Then at last Daedalus grew tired of the service of King Minos and longed to return to Athens, where he felt that his crime might have been forgotten or at least forgiven. He had brought with him to Crete his young son Icarus, and the boy too, now grown to manhood, wished to see his native land. But the craftsman could at first think of no way of escape. Crete was an island far distant from Athens, and Daedalus and his son could not build a ship in secrecy and man it for the voyage home. But his cunning brain was hard at work. At last he hit on the most daring invention of his life. Many an hour he had spent looking thoughtfully at the sea-birds as they wheeled and circled about the rocky coast. 'Ah,' said he, 'if only I could fly like them! But why not? The gods have not given men wings, but they have given them a brain and hands to fashion wings for themselves.'

So in a secret place, hidden from idle curiosity, he collected together all the feathers of birds he could find, great and small. He sent his son Icarus about the island to bring back as many as he could. Then he laid them out on the ground in order – first the big feathers, then the small. When he decided he had enough, he fastened them together with wax, curving the wings like those of a bird. Icarus watched his father intently. At last the wings were finished, and Daedalus strapped them to his shoulders and went up to a piece of rising ground. Turning into the wind, he ran forward and was delighted to find himself airborne. Day after day he practised on higher and higher slopes until he reckoned the time had come to make the flight to Greece. He constructed a second pair of wings for Icarus, and together the young man and his father mastered the art of flying.

At last the day of departure came. The sun was high in the unclouded heavens, and the wind was favourable. Daedalus and Icarus carried their wings to a lofty cliff looking towards Greece and prepared for flight. When the wings were strapped firmly on their backs, Daedalus said to his son:

'Follow me. Do as I do. Don't fly too low or your wings will be weighed down with spray from the sea. Don't fly too near the sun either, or its heat will melt the wax that holds the feathers in place. Either way you will be destroyed. Do as I say, and may the gods go with you. Now let us be off.'

So saying, he ran towards the edge of the cliff and launched himself into the air. Borne up by the wind, he journeyed straight towards his native shore.

Icarus did just as his father had done. But he was so happy to find himself aloft in the pure blue sky that he soon forgot the good advice he had been given. He wheeled and dipped like a great sea-bird, and then he soared upwards till the land and even the sea were almost out of sight. How brilliant the blazing sun appeared! Icarus was fascinated by it and could not withstand the temptation to see how high he could fly. Hotter and hotter it blazed down upon him. Too late he felt the wax on his wings begin to melt. He could not descend fast enough for the wax to cool. The wings that had borne him aloft now began to break up, and soon the ill-fated young man plunged helplessly into the sea, like a falling star. Icarus was drowned.

Daedalus had crossed the Aegean Sea and was almost home to Athens before he turned to catch sight of his son. Icarus was not to be seen. In alarm Daedalus turned and flew back to the south. It was not long before he saw, as he swooped down towards the blue waves, a pair of damaged wings floating uselessly on the sea. In sorrow Daedalus returned to Athens alone. The sea where his son had met his death was named the Icarian Sea.

4

Phaeton's Journey

THE Greeks believed that many, many years ago the whole earth was threatened with destruction by being burnt up. This was due to the recklessness of one young man. Disaster was only prevented by the action of Zeus, chief of the gods. The young man's name was Phaeton, and he was the son of the god Apollo and a nymph, Clymene. Phaeton was proud of being the son of a god, but sometimes his friends made fun of him and said he was telling a lie. One day he became violently angry because a friend told him he was wrong and that his father was no god but an ordinary man. Phaeton rushed home to Clymene, his mother, and said:

'Mother, if I am truly, as you tell me, the son of the god Apollo, give me some proof of it. I am sick of having my friends tell me I am lying.'

For answer, Clymene spread her arms wide and gazed towards the sun.

'I call upon Apollo, the Sun god, to bear witness that he is the father of my child, Phaeton. If I am not speaking the truth, may this be the last day I shall see your light!'

Then she turned to Phaeton and said:

'But nothing is easier than to go and ask him yourself. Each day the Sun your father rises in India, the very next country to our own. Go and ask him yourself if he will own you as his son.'

Eagerly Phaeton did as his mother said, and at once began the journey eastwards to India.

The palace of Apollo the Sun god had been constructed by Daedalus and was one of his most splendid creations. It stood high upon columns, its lofty form shining with gold and diadems. Its ceilings were of whitest ivory and its doors of solid silver. Upon the walls were pictures and carvings representing the whole world – earth, sea and sky: the earth was shown as populated by men and beasts, the sea by fish, and the air by birds. On the ceiling was carved a representation of heaven with all its stars and planets.

Phaeton was overcome by the dazzling splendour and beauty of the palace, but he advanced boldly up the steps which led to the entrance. He strode through the halls until he neared the presence of the Sun. Then he was forced to stop, for the light that shone from the face of the god was unbearable.

Apollo, robed in a purple mantle, sat upon a throne which glittered with a thousand diamonds. About him stood the Days and the Seasons. The head of Spring was adorned with flowers. Summer wore a garland of ripe corn. The feet of Autumn were stained with the juice of purple grapes, and Winter's hair was white with snow and stiffened by frost.

From his throne Apollo saw with the eyes that see all the young man who stood at the far end of the throne-room. He called to him to say why he had come.

'O Apollo – Father!' cried the young man. 'Give me some proof by which I shall know that I have the right to call you Father. How may I know that I am your son?'

Then Apollo laid aside his flaming crown, so that his brightness was dimmed, and told Phaeton to come closer. He told him to name his mother and to speak of the land where he lived. The young man told him his own name and that of his mother and spoke of their native Greece, which lay to the west.

'I who see all things,' answered Apollo, 'declare that you are my true son. By the way of proof, ask for anything you wish, and it shall be given you.'

Now it was the practice of Apollo to drive a golden chariot each day once round the earth, and from his earliest years Phaeton had been fascinated to see it rise above the eastern horizon, soar higher and higher into the noonday sky and gradually disappear in the west. How glorious it would be, he thought, to drive such a superb chariot. This would be something to show his friends. Now was his chance.

'Father,' he said excitedly, 'will you grant me *any* wish I shall name?'

'Yes, my son,' Apollo answered gravely. 'Any wish.'

'Then,' Phaeton replied, 'I wish to be allowed to drive your chariot for one day only.'

Apollo's face became clouded with fear and dismay.

'Do not ask that, my son,' he begged. 'That is the one thing I cannot allow you to do. No man may drive my chariot. I alone can handle it. Zeus himself, who hurls the lightning-stroke, may not do it. No mere mortal could make such a journey in safety. The first part of the course is steep, and even the four horses of the sun can hardly climb so high. You have not the strength to urge them on. The middle part of the course is high. Even I am almost too dizzy to look down and see the whole earth and ocean laid out before me. But the last part is the worst of all, for the descent to the west is very steep, and the horses must be reined in with the powerful arms of a god, or they will rush headlong to destruction. Moreover, while my chariot moves over the heavens, they are

35

continuously turning, with all the stars in their constellations. Unless I am perpetually on my guard, I too might be whirled away and lost for ever among the farthest constellations. You are young and without experience. How could you manage to make such a journey, even for one day? How could you keep to your course while the heavens are circling about you? There are no landmarks to guide you, as on a journey upon earth. My horses, too, are full of fire, and even I can scarcely control them. My son, I beg you to take back your wish before it is too late. If you seek proof that I am truly your father, you have only to look into my face and see the fear which your request causes me. Only a true father could so fear for a son's safety. If you could see into my heart, you would want no further proof. Lastly, if you take back this dreadful request, I swear that there is nothing else on earth you may not have. You are asking for destruction, not honour. Be advised by me and choose some other favour.'

But Phaeton was deaf to his father's entreaties and remained stubborn to the end. The more his father told him of the dangers of the journey, the more keenly he longed to make it. At last, with a heart full of foreboding, Apollo was forced to give in. He had pledged his word. Not even a god may break his word. How else would men trust him? He led his son to where the chariot was waiting.

The chariot, like the palace, was the work of Daedalus and was of pure gold. The wheels were golden, running upon silver axles. The body of the car was studded with brilliant jewels which reflected the beams of the sun with blinding brilliance. Phaeton was speechless with wonder. Even as he gazed, the gateways of the east were opened, and the stars of night retreated. It was time for the day's journey to begin. Apollo ordered the Hours to harness the flaming steeds, which were already snorting and stamping in their eagerness to be on their way.

Then Apollo took oil and bathed the face and shoulders of his son to protect him from the heat of the journey. As he set his helmet of light on the young man's head, he said:

'This at least remember. Whatever you do, use the reins more than the whip. These animals need holding in, not urging forward. Go not to the north nor to the south, but keep a middle course. Do not go too high or you will burn the mansions of the gods in heaven: do not go too low or you may set the earth on fire. Safety lies only in a middle course. If you are determined to make this journey, go now, and may all the gods assist you.'

Phaeton thanked his father and leaped into the chariot, grasping the reins in his left hand and the whip in his right. Instantly the horses bounded forwards and upwards. They soon knew that an inexperienced driver was holding the reins, and the chariot was jerked and jolted this way and that, from one side of the course to the other. As they rose on high, far higher than was safe, Phaeton was overcome. Gone were his pride and confidence in himself. All he could do was to hope he might learn to hold the powerful horses in check before disaster overtook him. But as he looked up at the heavens and then down at the earth spread far beneath him, his heart was filled with misgivings, his legs shook, his head felt dizzy. He began to wish he had never known of his father, never desired a thing so rash and perilous as to undertake a task which belonged only to a god. Why had he not been content to remain on earth, humbly, and live like other men?

Then he knew that he had lost all power to manage the flaming steeds. As the journey proceeded, their course became wilder and wilder. Up rose the chariot to the very

summit of heaven, only to plunge faster and faster towards
the earth. Phaeton was like a mariner in a storm-broken sea
who has given up all hope of deliverance. In his panic and
terror he let go the reins, and now there was no hand to check
or guide the horses. As they sped towards the west, close to
the earth's surface, whole forests caught fire. Trees were
scorched like straw. Even rocks melted. Seas, lakes and rivers
dried up and vanished in a puff of steam. Nothing could
withstand the terrible intensity of the Sun's heat. Worse than
all this, towns and cities were burnt to the ground. Men,
women and children, as well as animals, were unable to escape
the fire. Hills were reduced to ashes. The great forest-clad
ranges, the highest in the world, were set on fire, Athos and
Taurus, Caucasus, Atlas, and the mountains of Greece –
Helicon, Parnassus, Olympus. All flamed and cracked like
wheatfields in autumn struck by lightning. Even the greatest
rivers dried up in their beds – Ganges, Tigris and Euphrates.

In Egypt the Nile fled underground to escape the fierceness of the flames. The water-nymphs and the fishes swam to the very lowest depths of the sea or into its deepest caverns to shelter from the heat. Phaeton, scarcely able to breathe and blinded by scorching smoke, had abandoned all hope of regaining the mastery of his terrible steeds. He gave himself up for lost and could only pray that his end would be quick.

Earth herself, fearful of total destruction, at last raised her head and called to Zeus.

'O father of the gods,' Earth cried, 'from the beginning of time I have supplied men and animals with grass and plants, and with my aid alone have men been able to sacrifice to you and your fellow-gods. My surface is now all scorched, and it seems that I, like all else, will be utterly consumed. It may be your will that we must perish, but if we do, the heavens themselves will fall and all creation be ruined. I am faint and can say no more. My brother the Sea will soon be burnt up, and heaven itself will be destroyed and with it you and all the gods.'

Zeus heard the words of Earth. He called all the gods together and told them that, unless they acted, the whole of creation would come to an end. A stop must be put to the reckless course of the Sun's chariot. A screen of clouds must be raised in heaven to protect the earth from the Sun's heat. But no clouds remained. All had been burnt up in the chariot's mad course through the heavens. So Zeus himself, and he alone, could save the world. Standing on the highest mountain that had escaped destruction, he hurled a thunderbolt directly at Phaeton in the chariot. The young man, half-dead already from suffocation and weariness, was set on fire by the thunderbolt and fell headlong to the earth. As he fell, he looked like a shooting star. Straight into the waters of the River Eridanus he dropped. The river, though its waters were dwindled, had escaped the worst of the heat. Phaeton was drowned.

Zeus, meanwhile, had summoned Apollo the Sun god to come at once and take charge of the fiery chariot, which was now riderless. Apollo, grieving bitterly at the terrible end which had befallen his beloved son, summoned all his strength, gained control of his weary horses and drove them back to their stables in the east.

So ended Phaeton's journey, undertaken through stubborn pride against the advice of his father. The nymphs of the river raised a monument to his memory and inscribed upon it these words:

'Under this stone lies Phaeton, son of Apollo, who tried in vain to drive his father's chariot across the sky.'

Phaeton's sisters, the Heliades, stood round the spot where their brother had fallen, weeping and lamenting. There they remained until the gods, taking pity on their inconsolable grief, turned them into a grove of poplar trees.

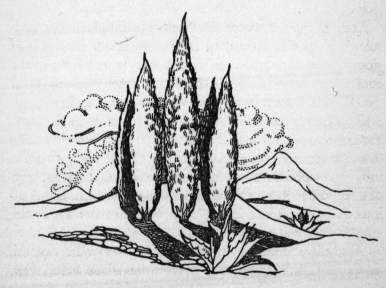

5

King Midas

1 The Golden Touch

MIDAS, king of Phrygia, was born to be rich. When he was a baby, his nurse noticed a long line of ants climbing up into his cradle. Each ant carried a grain of wheat which it dropped into the baby's mouth. At once the palace magicians were sent for, and they had no difficulty in explaining this extra-ordinary event. The ears of golden grain, they said, stood for riches. Certainly the little prince was destined to be one of the richest kings in the world.

And so it turned out. Midas grew up into a pleasure-loving ruler. His palace, one of the most splendid ever fashioned, stood in the midst of a wonderful rose-garden. The air was cooled by ever-flowing fountains, and there were miles of tree-shaded walks about the palace.

One dewy morning Midas rose early to walk in his gardens. He was surprised to hear the sound of snoring and wheezing from among the rose-trees. Then he saw an old fat man lying full length upon the grass, breathing heavily in the deep sleep of utter contentment. Evidently some old reveller had strayed into the palace grounds the night before, to sleep off the effects of too much wine.

This indeed turned out to be the truth. The reveller, as soon as he was awake, confessed that he was none other than

Silenus, the old schoolmaster and companion of the god Dionysus. He had wandered away from the main party after the feasting of the night before, and stumbled into Midas's rose-garden. Here he tripped over a grassy mound and instantly fell asleep under a sweet-smelling rose. The smell of the rose mingled with the fumes of the wine; and the elderly Silenus, his ruddy face wreathed in flowers, struck the king as a touching and pathetic figure. Midas, recognizing Silenus for a lover of pleasure like himself, invited him to stay at the palace. The old fellow was only too happy to do so. Ten days he spent with the king, feasting and drinking and telling gay, lively stories from morning till night.

Meanwhile, the god Dionysus had become anxious about the loss of his old tutor and companion, whose company he loved dearly. So he sent servants to explore the countryside near where they had been revelling together. On the eleventh day servants reached the palace of Midas and were rewarded by the news that Silenus was safe and in good health, enjoying the king's hospitality.

Unwillingly Midas said farewell to his guest, who thanked him for his kindness and returned with the servants to Dionysus. The god was so delighted at the safe return of his old companion and so grateful to Midas for befriending him that he sent messengers to the king to offer him a reward.

'Ask for anything you wish, O king,' said the chief of the messengers, 'and your wish shall be granted.'

Now Midas, rich as he was, had no other ambition than to be even richer. Without a second thought he replied:

'Give thanks to your master, the great Dionysus, and tell him that my dearest wish would be to have everything that I touch turn into pure gold.'

When Dionysus heard this request, he frowned.

'That is a foolish wish,' he said, 'and he will be sorry for it.'

Then with a shrug of his shoulders he added, 'But if that is what he wants, let him have it. Men should learn to wish for the right things.'

Next day Midas was walking in the palace grounds. Idly he broke off a twig from a low-growing oak-tree. Instantly it was turned into pure gold and glittered with a soft, pale radiance.

'My wish has been granted!' he exclaimed. 'How beautiful – and what wealth I shall have! Why, I shall be the richest king in the world.'

Scarcely able to believe his good fortune, Midas bent down and picked up a stone. At once it was turned to gold. Then he touched a clod of earth, a spray of leaves, a lizard asleep in the sun. All became gold at his touch. An apple that he plucked from a tree, transformed at once into shining metal, was like the legendary apples that grow in the Hesperides, the gardens of the west. Midas's delight knew no bounds. As soon as he got back to the palace, he ordered a sumptuous banquet to be prepared, that he might rejoice in the fortune that had fallen upon him, and render thanks to the god of feasting and merriment. The banquet was prepared. Midas sat down at the head of the table amidst his admiring courtiers.

'Let us eat and drink,' he cried, 'and give thanks to Dionysus!'

Looking round him at the assembled company, his face wreathed in smiles and his head in garlands of ivy and myrtle, he took a piece of bread from the dish before him and raised it to his lips. Horror-struck, he found that the bread was turned to solid gold. The smile died on his face. He put out his hand for meat. It too became gold. In desperation he clutched at a goblet of rich wine to quench his thirst. As soon as the wine touched his lips, a stream of liquid gold began to flow down his throat. At last he realized that everything he tried to eat or

drink would be turned to metal, and he must soon face death by starvation. How much he would have given to be able to taste even a stale crust or a cup of water!

'The king is ill,' said the courtiers. 'Let us leave him to himself and go home.'

So the guests departed, leaving Midas pale and distracted.

'Oh, what a fool I was to ask for such a gift! This golden touch will be my ruin. What is the use of all the gold in the world if I am to die for lack of food and drink?'

So Midas raised his arms to the sky and begged the great Dionysus to take away the terrible power he had granted. Dionysus was a kindly and merciful god, and he consented to do as Midas begged.

'He has learned his lesson,' he said to himself, 'and perhaps in future he will not set such store by mere gold.'

Then he spoke directly to Midas from on high.

'Go, unhappy king,' he said, 'to the country of Lydia, and

trace the River Pactolus to its spring. When you have found it, wash your head and your body in its streams, and you will be cleansed, both of the desire for wealth and of your punishment.'

Midas hurried to do as he was bid. Taking servants with him, he went to Lydia and found the source of the River Pactolus. When he had washed himself thoroughly in its waters, he found, to his infinite comfort, that he no longer had the golden touch. The leaves, when he fingered them, remained green and supple. Stones remained stones and water water. Gratefully he drank of the cooling stream and swallowed some food that his servants had brought. But the golden touch had passed into the waters of the Pactolus, so that, from that day to this, the river has always flowed over golden sands.

Midas felt as if he had awoken from a bad dream. Not only had he lost the golden touch; he had lost all desire for riches. The precious metal became to him a hateful thing.

2 A Pair of Ass's Ears

IN a wild part of Greece called Arcadia dwelt the god Pan. Some say he was the son of Hermes, others that he was the son of Zeus. Like a satyr, he had goat's feet, on which he was able to move swiftly over the rocks and hills. He had fallen in love with the nymph Syrinx. But she had no wish to be pursued by the goat-footed god, and had turned herself into a reed. Pan cut the reed into seven pipes of unequal length and fastened them side by side with wax. Then he put the pipes to his mouth and blew into them. The first tune he played was a lament for the loss of Syrinx. Sadly and sweetly it sounded among the vales and woods of Arcadia.

Then the shepherd boys and girls who roamed about the meadows looking after their sheep often heard the music of Pan's pipes, though he was rarely seen, so nimbly did he move about the woods and hills on his goat's feet. So they

became afraid of him; and when any of them found himself struck by a sudden fear, he could not tell why, he would say he was in the presence of the unseen god. And from that time to this men have called this nameless fear a 'panic'.

Nevertheless, the shepherds and shepherdesses loved their god Pan. They set up stone altars and temples in his name. They made sacrifices to him and sang and danced in his honour.

King Midas, once he had lost the golden touch and all desire for riches, wandered about Arcadia and became a worshipper of Pan. He wore simple clothes of sheepskin and joined the shepherds in their songs and dances. He loved to roam beside the woodland streams at dawn or dusk in the hope of hearing the unearthly music of the pipes. In time he came to think of it as the most beautiful music in all the world.

Now Apollo the Sun god was looked on as the greatest of all musicians. The instrument he played was the lyre. It was made from the shell of a tortoise, across which were stretched seven strings, and was played either by plucking them with the fingers or by striking them with a piece of bone called a plectrum.

The reverence paid to Pan by the simple country people of Arcadia had made the god proud, so that he decided to challenge Apollo to a contest, in order to prove that he, Pan, was champion among musicians. Apollo readily accepted the challenge, and the mountain god Tmolus was chosen as judge. Tmolus sat enthroned on his mountain, surrounded by pine trees. As Pan began to play his strange and plaintive pipe-music, the trees bent to one side to let Tmolus hear better. Midas had come to listen to the contest, certain that his beloved Pan would be the victor. When Pan had finished, both he and Midas were very satisfied with his performance.

Tmolus said nothing, but looked towards the Sun god, and all the trees turned their heads too.

Apollo stood on Mount Parnassus, robed in purple and crowned with a laurel wreath. Then, having tuned his lyre, he held it in his left hand and swept the strings with his right. A hush fell upon the audience. While he played, all were silent, overcome with admiration at the wonderful harmonies which came from the seven-stringed lyre. As soon as he had finished, shouts of applause broke out, and Tmolus had no hesitation in declaring Apollo winner. From that time on, it was always Apollo who was chosen to play at the feasts of the gods, who never failed to be ravished by his mighty music.

The judgement satisfied everyone except Midas. No sooner had Tmolus's decision been made known than he rushed up and loudly protested.

'The victory should have gone to Pan!' Midas cried. 'His is the finest music ever heard by human ears.'

At once everyone laughed, and Apollo in anger decided to punish Midas for his rash judgement.

'Foolish man,' he said, 'if that is what you think, you no longer deserve to have human ears.'

Instantly Midas felt his ears become long and pointed and covered with thick coarse hair inside and out. He was able to twitch and turn them in any direction. He had been given the ears of an ass. In vain did Midas pray to his god Pan to remove from him this terrible affliction, for he knew it would make him a laughing-stock everywhere he went. But Pan had no power to undo a punishment imposed by Apollo.

So Midas did the best he could to hide his shame. Whenever he appeared in public, he wore a tall head-dress in the form of a turban, which completely hid his ears from sight. But there was one man from whom he could not hide them. This was, of course, the hairdresser who from time to time had the task of cutting and trimming Midas's hair. He commanded the man, on pain of death, never to tell anyone about the ass's ears. The hairdresser promised, and for a time he dared not utter the secret even to himself.

But who can keep a secret for ever? One day the hairdresser felt an irresistible urge to whisper the king's secret. Afraid to tell it in public, he went to a lonely place beside a stream, dug a hole in the ground and said into it:

'Midas has ass's ears!'

Then he filled up the hole and left the place as fast as he could, thinking his secret was safe.

There is not much more to tell. Very soon a bed of rushes sprang up where the hole had been, and when they were tall enough they began to rustle in the wind. Whenever a breeze passed over them, they would whisper:

'Midas has ass's ears – Midas has ass's ears!'

So any shepherd boy or girl who happened to stray by that stream when a breeze was blowing might hear the secret of poor Midas's shame.

6

Jason and the Argonauts

1 The Boyhood of Jason

THERE was once a king of Thessaly who had two children, a boy called Phrixus and a girl called Helle. After a time this king Athamas married a new wife; this stepmother was a wicked woman, and hated the children and planned to kill them. But the gods took pity on them and Hermes, messenger of the gods, sent a wonderful creature, a ram with a long fleece of pure gold. On its back their mother Nephele set her two children, Phrixus and Helle, who nestled together in the silky fleece. Almost at once the ram rose in the air, and was soon lost to sight. Nephele knew that the creature had been sent from the gods, and she believed it would take her children to a place of safety.

The ram flew eastward towards the Black Sea, but when it was over the narrow straits at the mouth of the sea, the little girl grew sleepy and fell off the ram's back into the water. So ever afterwards this place was known as Hellespont. Phrixus, who had not been able to save his sister, clung all the more tightly to the ram's fleece, and was carried safely over the southern shore of the Black Sea. Below him he saw the fishermen's boats on the water, the wide mouths of rivers flowing down from the hills through the dark pine woods. At last they reached the far end of the Black Sea and came down in the land of Colchis.

The king of Colchis was named Aëtes. He received the boy hospitably, for he knew that the flying ram must have been sent by the gods. Phrixus offered the ram as a sacrifice to Zeus, father of the gods, in thanksgiving for his safe arrival in Colchis. The golden fleece was given into the keeping of Aëtes, who had it hung in a tree in the middle of a grove consecrated to Zeus. Around the trunk of this tree was coiled a great serpent to protect it from any who might come to steal it. Aëtes was very proud of this treasure. It pleased him and his people to see the golden fleece gleaming through the leaves in the level rays of the setting sun.

The fame of the fleece spread far and wide. One of the places it reached was the kingdom of Iolcos, where reigned an old king called Aeson. Growing weary of ruling the country, Aeson surrendered his crown to his brother Pelias, who was younger than he. Aeson had a son named Jason, and when he gave up his kingdom to Pelias, he made it a condition that it was to be given to Jason when the boy came of age.

Now Aeson grew afraid that some harm might come to Jason, so he sent him away to be brought up in the mountains. Jason's tutor and guardian was Chiron, one of the strangest creatures imaginable. He was a centaur – one whose head and shoulders are those of a man and his body that of a white horse. Chiron thus combined the strength and grace of a horse with the wisdom of a man. He was wise in all the arts, especially those of music, medicine and archery. All of these things he taught to his young pupil, who could not have had a better master. Chiron was indeed the teacher of many famous men. One of these was Asclepius, who was later worshipped as the god of healing; another was the great Achilles, who slew Hector at the siege of Troy. For years Jason grew up in safety, competing in friendly rivalry with the other boys in Chiron's charge. He learned to shoot straight, to swim, to run and to wrestle; he learned how to read the stars, to understand music, mathematics and poetry. Above all, he learned to be dutiful to the gods and to make sacrifices to them on the appointed days. He became stronger, more handsome and graceful in movement than any of Chiron's pupils. By the time he reached manhood, it was known to everyone that he was destined for some great adventure.

'Before I leave you, master,' he said to Chiron, 'I must thank you for all you have done for me. No young man, I am sure, ever had a better teacher. Give me, I beg, one last piece of advice. How shall I determine what to do with my life?'

'I think,' answered Chiron, looking at Jason with his wise, kindly eyes, 'you will have a life full of adventure and even of danger. The gods intended you for great enterprises. Only they can tell you what to do. Go and consult the priests in the temple of Zeus.'

Jason did as he was bidden, and the priests told him it was the will of the gods that, being now a man, he should return to Iolcos and claim the kingdom as his own.

So the young man said goodbye to his tutor and set off on his journey.

Over hill and valley he travelled, scaling rocky cliffs, scrambling through dense forests, slithering down the narrow tracks made by the mountain goats. When he came to a river, he forded or swam it. One such river ran across his path as he was nearing Iolcos. He was about to plunge into the swift water when he saw an old woman on the bank.

'Help me across, young man,' the woman begged. 'I am old, and you have enough strength for two.'

In spite of the woman's torn garments and the scars and wrinkles in her weathered face, Jason was aware of something queenly in her eyes and bearing.

'As you will, mother,' he said courteously.

He crouched low at the water's edge and took her on his back. Then he dived into the stream and struggled as best he could towards the farther side. He found his passenger unexpectedly heavy, so that he was obliged to battle fiercely with the rushing water. In doing so he lost one of his sandals. When he reached the bank, he set the old woman down and searched for his sandal. But the stream had already carried it out of reach, and he must go to Iolcos as best he could with only one sandal. Looking around to make sure that the woman was safe, Jason was surprised to find that she had utterly vanished. Then he knew that she must be a goddess in disguise. She was indeed Hera, queen of the gods, who had come to help the young man, because Pelias had neglected her worship in Iolcos.

As soon as Jason set foot in the city, the people gathered round to gaze at the handsome stranger who had suddenly

appeared in their midst. They admired his tall, youthful figure, his bronzed face, and the fearless, challenging look in his eyes. Pelias the king, too, admired Jason. But he also had cause to be afraid of him. For one of the first things he noticed about the young stranger was that he had only one sandal. The other foot was bare. Pelias remembered – indeed he had never forgotten – that it had long ago been foretold how a man with only one sandal would come to claim his kingdom.

Jason left him in no doubt as to the reason for his coming. When Pelias asked him why he had come to Iolcos, he said boldly and without hesitation, for all to hear:

'I am your nephew Jason. I have reached years of manhood, and I claim this kingdom as my right. I demand its surrender.'

At this all the people murmured their approval. Some raised a cheer. They had no love for Pelias, and Jason had at once made a favourable impression.

'Give up the kingdom,' some said. 'We will have Jason for King.'

Pelias tugged at his beard and thought fast. He dared not challenge his nephew's claim to his kingdom in the face of all the people.

'My friends,' said Pelias calmly, 'you are right. My nephew has a royal bearing, and he is just in his demand. Nevertheless, it is better to be wise than to regret an error of haste. How can we be sure that the young man is fit to rule the kingdom? What act of heroism has he performed? What deed of valour or what noble adventure stands to his credit?'

'None as yet,' answered Jason with frankness, 'but I am ready to undertake any honourable enterprise you shall name.'

'Good,' said the crafty Pelias, for he had already formed a scheme by which his nephew might be destroyed. 'You have no doubt heard of the famous golden fleece which is said to be kept in Colchis. This trophy belongs by right to us, for the boy Phrixus was of our family. It should be kept here in Iolcos. It is too precious to remain with strangers in far-off Colchis. Go, Jason, and reclaim the golden fleece. There is an enterprise worthy of the future ruler of Iolcos. I will be proud to surrender the kingdom to you as soon as you return with the fleece.'

To get back the golden fleece was indeed an enterprise of great hardship and danger. But Jason readily accepted the challenge, and prepared to set out at once. How he started on his voyage, what adventures befell him, and how he fared in his mighty task – all this shall now be told. How years later the hero did indeed come home with honour, and how, sad to tell, he was in the end cheated of success through acts of enchantment – these things too must be related in order as they fell out.

2 Voyage of the Argo

JASON knew that the journey to Colchis would be long and dangerous. No Greek had ever before made such a long voyage by sea. So he decided to gather round him a company of young men of adventurous spirit to help him in his undertaking. He sent messengers all over the country to let it be known that he was looking for such companions. Meanwhile, he got a famous boat-builder named Argos to make a ship bigger and stronger than any that had ever before been seen in Greece. When it was finished, it was indeed a splendid craft. It had not only sails, but also benches for oarsmen. It looked swift as well as sturdy, and well fitted to battle with any wind or storm that might trouble the waters between Thessaly and the far end of the Black Sea. The ship was named the Argo, and the company that sailed in her were called the Argonauts.

When the Argonauts assembled, there were fifty-three men and one woman. Among the men were Orpheus, the greatest musician ever known; Heracles, noted for his enormous strength; Lynceus, whose sight was so keen that men said he could see through the earth; the twins, Castor and Pollux, sons of Zeus; and Asclepius, the doctor. Tiphys was the steersman, and the one woman was Atalanta, a swift runner and a great huntress.

As soon as the Argonauts had made sacrifices to the gods and prayed to them for help and guidance, they weighed anchor, and the oarsmen took the ship out of harbour. When they were in the open sea, Jason gave orders to hoist sail, ready to take advantage of a favourable wind. With Tiphys at the helm handling the rudder, and Orpheus at the prow singing and playing on his harp, the Argo was soon bounding over the blue waves.

Many were the adventures which befell Jason and his brave company before they reached their journey's end. It would take too long to recount them all. Before they had travelled far, they were obliged to stop at the island of Chios in order to take in water. Some of the men carried barrels ashore and began to fill them from the freshest streams they could find, but one of them went further inland than the others and was lost to view. This was a beautiful boy called Hylas, friend and favourite of the hero Heracles. Hylas strayed far inland to a pool sacred to the water-nymphs, who bathed in its depths and basked on its shady banks. Here grew lilies and poppies, and overhead hung delicious wild apples. Hylas was so enchanted with this pool that he lay down on the bank gazing into the water. When they saw the beautiful boy, the water-nymphs fell in love with him and gathered about him singing their strange songs or murmuring words of love. They dared

him to follow them into the water. Hylas could not resist, and dived after them into the cool, clear depths. No man ever saw him again. For long hours Heracles and his friends went about the island calling his name. 'Hylas! Hylas!' echoed through the woods, but there was no answer. Heracles could not bear to leave the place where his companion had disappeared. At last the Argonauts were forced to sail on, leaving behind the grief-stricken hero.

When they had lost the mighty Heracles, one of the strongest men left to the Argonauts was the boxer, Pollux. He and his brother Castor were twin sons of Zeus. The Argo sailed on until she reached the land of the Bebryces, a warlike people accustomed to handling very roughly any strangers who visited their shores. Their king was Amycus, son of the sea-god Poseidon. He was a huge, brawny man covered with black, bristling hair. It was his habit to challenge strangers to single combat in the boxing-ring. At the time of the Argonauts' arrival he had never once been beaten, and had made a slave of every one of his victims.

Immediately the Argo beached, Amycus sent his challenge. It was accepted by Pollux without hesitation. Argonauts and Bebryces gathered round an open space, and the two fighters faced one another. Pollux was scarcely more than half the weight of the giant Amycus; but he was nimble and quick-witted, while his brawny opponent, like many bullies, was slow and stupid. His fists were like legs of mutton, and one blow from either of them would have felled a bigger man than Pollux. So the son of Zeus took care to avoid those terrible fists. He danced skilfully around Amycus, getting in a blow when he could, and avoiding the other's aims. Every time he did so, there were cheers from the Argonauts and groans from the Bebryces. In this way Pollux began to tire his heavy opponent while remaining in fighting form himself. Once indeed his foot slipped, and Amycus came for him like an angry bull. But Pollux was on his feet once more just in time to step aside as Amycus, unable to stop himself, crashed into the wall of spectators at the edge of the ring.

At last the sun began to go down in the western sky, and the wily Pollux managed to manoeuvre so that its level rays shone full in his opponent's eyes. Amycus lunged wildly, and his heavy breathing told everyone that he was exhausted. Pollux knew that the decisive moment had come. Retreating a few steps, and keeping the sun always behind him, he flew at the weary giant and succeeded in landing a deadly blow with his right fist square on Amycus' left temple. It was the knock-out blow. Amycus groaned, and fell to the ground, unable to rise. Pollux might then have killed him, but he spared his life on condition that he released all whom he had enslaved and made a solemn promise not to battle with peaceable strangers who visited his country in the future. Then the Argonauts rejoiced in the victory of their hero, and the singer Orpheus composed a ballad in celebration of the event. Sacrifices were made to the gods, and the heroes returned to their ship, prepared to set sail in the morning.

Once again the Argo set sail and, with a fair wind following, made good speed towards the Black Sea. But before long the wind strengthened and, fearing a storm, Jason decided to put in at an island. Here reigned the blind King Phineus, who had the gift of prophecy. Because he had foretold secrets which men were not allowed to know, the gods punished him. He lost his sight and, worse even than that, he was never allowed a meal. Whenever food was served to him, strange beasts known as harpies pounced down upon the food and bore it away before Phineus could taste it. These harpies had the faces of cruel women and the bodies and claws of vultures, birds which prey upon dead bodies. Such was the greed of the

harpies that poor Phineus had scarcely enough food to keep soul and body together. Thin and wretched he looked in his blindness as he greeted the heroes from the Argo.

Jason took pity on him and determined to deliver him from his miserable condition. Among the Argonauts were two winged brothers, sons of the north wind, called Calais and Zetes. They agreed to chase the harpies away and fight them in mid-air. So a banquet was set before the King and, sure enough, no sooner had he sat down than there was a beating of wings and a greedy screaming from the air, and three harpies alighted on the table and began to carry off the food. Calais and Zetes chased them from the table and pursued them into the air, brandishing their sharp swords. Twist and turn as they might, the harpies were not swift enough to get away from the sons of the north wind, who followed them over hill and forest, up into the very clouds. There they would certainly have been slaughtered had not Iris, goddess of the rainbow, stretched out her arms to save them. She forbade Calais and Zetes to kill the harpies, but promised that, as a reward for the courage of the two Argonauts, the harpies would stop persecuting King Phineus. So the creatures flew off, uttering their hateful cries, in pursuit of other prey, while Calais and Zetes returned to their companions. All sat down to the banquet that had been prepared, and for the first time for many years Phineus was allowed to eat in peace.

Jason decided to ask Phineus, who had prophetic powers, to tell him of the dangers in store for him on his expedition to regain the golden fleece.

'Ah, my son,' said the blind prophet, 'the greatest of your dangers awaits you in Colchis itself, but of this I may not speak, for I do not wish to anger the gods a second time. Before you reach the Black Sea, however, a danger awaits you which is serious enough.'

'Tell us of it,' said Jason, 'so that we need not meet it unprepared.'

'At the mouth of the straits leading to the Black Sea,' answered King Phineus, 'you must pass between the Symplegades. These are two great rocks or cliffs which clash together, and whatever is caught between them, whether a bird or a boat, is instantly crushed and shattered, like corn between two millstones.'

'This is a danger indeed,' said Jason gravely. 'How may we overcome it?'

'Sail on bravely,' said the king, 'until you come within sight of the rocks. Then release a white pigeon, and if it flies between the rocks in safety, that is a sign that the gods are pleased with your enterprise and will allow your ship to pass through. That is all I can tell you.'

Next day Jason and his companions took leave of King Phineus and thanked him for his advice. Then they boarded the Argo, bent their backs to the oars and, steered by the skilful Tiphys, made their way out of the harbour. On shore they could see the smoke rising from the thank-offerings they had sacrificed to the gods. The storm they had feared passed over during the night, so that now there was no more than a fresh breeze to fill their sails and carry them on.

For days the Argonauts sped eastward through calm water. With Orpheus singing at the prow and the sturdy heroes managing the sails, the great ship ploughed a straight furrow towards the entrance to the Black Sea. Daily they got nearer to the danger of which they had been warned. Then one day, about noon, keen-eyed Lynceus, who had been posted as lookout, discerned a patch of churning white water eight or nine miles ahead. Clearly he saw it against the blue waters that lay all around. Half an hour later he made out the tall, rocky forms of the dreaded Symplegades.

'The clashing rocks!' he shouted. 'Rocks ahead! We are sailing straight towards them.'

The Argonauts crowded to the prow. There was no doubt of what Lynceus had told them. They were approaching the rocks. As they drew nearer, Jason ordered the sails to be lowered, as a precaution against being carried too close by a sudden wind. Then he told every oarsman to be ready in his place and await the moment when they must drive the ship forward with all their strength. The rocks loomed ahead; the waves boiled angrily at their base as they swung together, crashed into one another, and drew apart. The noise was like thunder. It seemed as if the sky was split open and Zeus himself was roaring with fury.

Jason had not forgotten to capture a white pigeon and put it in a cage of wickerwork before they left the country of King

Phineus. When the ship was as near to the rocks as he judged it safe to go, Jason opened the cage and released the bird. Straight and fast it flew towards the narrow gap between the rocks. The Argonauts held their breath, shuddering with dread as the rocks swung together. Then the crash came, and every man strained his eyes for a sight of the pigeon. As soon as he could make himself heard once more, Jason cried to everyone to bend to his oar and await the command to row. Then, when in a few moments the gap of blue sky could once more be seen widening between the dreadful jaws of rock, the tiny white creature was seen winging its way eastward. It was free, but a white feather fluttered down from its tail to show how narrowly it had escaped destruction.

'Now!' roared Jason. 'Row for your lives! Row as you never rowed before!'

Every man bent his back and strained to his oar, as if he would crack his very sinews. Like a racehorse when the starter gives his signal, the great ship leapt forward, plunging through the churning waves straight into the jaws of the Symplegades. Tiphys with two of his fellows clung firmly to the helm lest the raging waters should wrench it from their grasp. The ship's timbers cracked and groaned as she was urged onwards by the heaving arms of the rowers. Jason prayed to his protectress Hera as the Argo was driven into the terrible chasm which, any second, might close and crush them all to pieces like a helpless rabbit in the jaws of a lion.

But the gods were favourable to Jason and his companions. They spared the Argo as they had spared the white pigeon. Yet the heroes were as near to death as the bird had been; for when the ship slid between the Symplegades, which at once clashed together behind it, it was found that the rearmost end of the rudder had been crushed and splintered by the rocks. This was the only damage suffered by either ship or men.

3 The Golden Fleece

AS the Argonauts rowed into the open waters of the Black Sea, the sails were hoisted once more, so that the heroes might rest their tired bodies while the wind from the west drove them on towards Colchis. In due course they reached the kingdom of Aëtes, who was surprised to see such an impressive expedition land upon his shore. He greeted the strangers courteously; and when they had feasted and made sacrifices to the gods, Aëtes asked them their business.

Jason answered boldly, as was his custom:

'King Aëtes,' he said, 'for years you have held the miraculous golden fleece which was offered to Zeus by my kinsman Phrixus. Now that I am come to manhood, I claim the fleece as my prize, to be carried back to my native kingdom of Iolcos in Thessaly. I trust you will surrender me the trophy without ill-will or resistance.'

King Aëtes' brow darkened, for he was proud of the fleece and unwilling to give it up to this young stranger. But he looked upon the heroes with their strong arms and resolute faces and thought it prudent to make a soft answer.

'You shall have the fleece,' he replied, 'but first, in order to show you are a worthy guardian of so splendid a treasure, you must perform certain tasks. Tomorrow at sunrise you must go out and yoke two of my famous brazen bulls whose nostrils breathe fire and smoke.'

At this Jason's followers looked aghast, for how was any man to set a yoke on the necks of such terrible creatures? But Jason said nothing, and continued to regard the king without flinching.

'Next,' continued Aëtes, 'you must plough a field with these same bulls and sow it all over with the dragon's teeth which you will be given. Finally, you must take the golden fleece single-handed from the tree where it is guarded by the serpent in the grove sacred to Zeus. Only then may you claim the prize for your own.'

Those who observed the king closely might have seen the look of cunning which lurked in his dark eyes as he pronounced these conditions. Would not any man be mad, murmured the Colchians among themselves, to accept such conditions? For even if Jason could yoke the flaming bulls and plough and sow the field, how was he, single-handed, to drag the fleece from the care of the terrible serpent coiled around the tree? The young stranger must surely be going to his death.

That evening Aëtes' beautiful daughter Medea went to pay her nightly sacrifice to Hecate, the goddess of witchcraft. For Medea was an enchantress and had secret knowledge and secret powers denied to ordinary mortals. She had been thinking about the handsome young leader of the Greeks and about the terrible fate that awaited him next day. She knew that without magical help he could never accomplish the tasks her father had set him; she knew too that her father wished to destroy Jason. Her heart was filled with pity, for she had fallen in love with the stranger as soon as she set eyes on him. Never before had such a resolute and fearless man come to Colchis. But if Medea were to help Jason by means of her magic powers, how could she face her father? If Jason were not destroyed by the fiery bulls or the serpent, Aëtes would know that it was she, his own daughter, who had helped him. Then her father would destroy her.

But when, returning from the sacrifices to Hecate, she saw Jason walking alone, love overcame her fear of her father, and she made up her mind to help him.

'You do not know the danger you are in,' she told him.

'How will you manage to yoke my father's bulls, which no man has ever handled before?'

'Will you help me, beautiful princess?' asked Jason.

'If I do,' replied Medea, 'I will have to flee, or my father will put me to death. He does not mean you to have the golden fleece.'

'If you help me to gain the fleece,' said Jason, 'you shall go with me on the Argo and become my wife. You shall reign with me in Iolcos.'

'That is a bargain,' agreed Medea. 'I will now tell you what you must do tomorrow. First, you must gather herbs with me, as I shall instruct you.'

So they gathered herbs, for Medea, being an enchantress, knew which had magic power. By nightfall they had gathered enough for Medea's purpose, choosing only those which were for protection. Of these Medea made a magical drink of great power. She told Jason to take this before going to sleep. Then she gave him other instructions and wished him goodnight.

Next day at sunrise all the people, Greeks and Colchians, gathered round the field of Ares, god of war, where Jason was to sow the dragon's teeth. In one corner the plough was ready. There was a gasp of fear, and all drew back as two brazen-hoofed bulls were let loose. Their nostrils gushed fire and black smoke; their metal horns gleamed cruelly in the morning sun. They pawed the earth menacingly as the intrepid young man moved towards them. It seemed impossible that any human being could live within reach of these awful beasts. Jason would be scorched to death the moment he came near them. But, protected by Medea's charms, he strode boldly up to the bulls, put his arms about their necks and began to stroke their dewlaps and pat their glossy shoulders. The smoke and flame from their nostrils licked harmlessly about his face and breast. The onlookers gasped with amazement as Jason slipped the wooden yoke about their docile necks and led them to the plough.

Straight and true, Jason drove the first furrow along the edge of the field, and it was not long before the whole space was covered with brown new-turned earth. Everyone marvelled to see such fine ploughing.

Hiding his anger, King Aëtes gave him a leather bag containing dragon's teeth. At once Jason began striding up and down the furrows, scattering the teeth as he went.

As soon as they were sown, a host of fully armed soldiers sprang out of the ground and faced the hero with raised weapons and threatening looks. From every tooth had grown an armed man. The spectators cowered back in terror. Jason alone looked at the army without flinching. Medea had told him what he must do. Single-handed and unarmed, he waited till the soldiers began to move towards him. Then he stopped and lifted a boulder from the edge of the field. With all his might he hurled the stone missile through the air. It landed near the rear of the armed men, striking one of them to the ground. From where he had been standing, the soldier could not see where the stone had come from; thinking it had been thrown by one of his companions he leapt to his feet and struck at the nearest man. In hitting back, the second man caught his neighbour a blow. Instantly his neighbour struck out, and a fierce battle began. Swords slashed, spears flew through the air; the whole field was loud with the din of armour and the groans of wounded men. Jason prudently stepped back among the Argonauts while the soldiers who had sprung from the dragon's teeth slaughtered each other. They had no leader, no general to order them to end the battle; so that, before an hour had passed, scarcely a soldier remained alive. Over the dead and dying the Greeks exulted, cheering their hero to the skies, while even the Colchians, despite the anger of their king, joined in the applause. Medea, pale with anxiety, looked in fear towards her father, wondering if he suspected her treachery. But all Aëtes could say was, 'Now let us see how he will handle the serpent. That will surely be the end of him.'

Medea, who had been praying to Hecate for the safety of her lover, slipped away from her father and reached the sacred grove where the serpent guarded the golden fleece. The Greeks went with Jason to the grove, and there they saw the trophy gleaming through the leaves. At the foot of the tree where it hung was the terrible serpent. Its barbed crest, fierce claws and three-pronged tongue, ready to dart poison at any who molested it, struck terror into the hearts of all. But Jason went boldly up to it, taking from his wallet the magic herbs that Medea had given him. These he scattered all round and over the beast, murmuring a powerful spell he had learned from the enchantress. Gradually the serpent grew weary, closed its eyes and fell asleep.

As soon as Jason saw that it could do him no harm, he reached up into the tree and unhooked the fleece. Then he spoke a prayer to Zeus and strode swiftly out of the grove, followed by the Greeks and Medea. By this time night had fallen, and in the darkness they made for the harbour and prepared to sail at once in the Argo, for fear that Aëtes would attempt to stop their departure by some further trick. Jason found that Medea was by his side. He took her aboard, and as soon as the last of the Argonauts was safe in the ship, they weighed anchor, bent to the oars, and made off as fast as they were able. Back they sailed westwards to the Hellespont and the coasts of Thessaly, as fast as sail and oar could carry them.

Aëtes, indeed, enraged by the loss of the fleece and the flight of his daughter, did pursue Jason. Putting to sea with a fleet of smaller boats, he pursued the heroes for many leagues. Gradually his ships gained on the fleeing Argo, and then Medea had her young brother Absyrtus put to death and his body cut in pieces. His limbs were scattered on the waves, and the boy's horrified father, Aëtes, when he reached the place, stopped to gather up his son's remains and give them a decent burial on shore. In this way Aëtes was forced to give up the chase, and the Argo was left to sail in triumph back to Iolcos. Jason's adventure was concluded; he had the prize he had sought for so long; in addition he had brought home a beautiful bride to reign with him over the kingdom he was now to claim from his uncle Pelias.

The return of Jason and the Argonauts was celebrated with bonfires and sacrifices, music and feasting. It would be pleasant to think that the story ended happily, but the gods willed otherwise. It is true that Medea had helped Jason, but she was an enchantress and had come from a wild and barbarous people. Out of vengeance against Pelias for having kept Jason so long from his kingdom, she had Pelias put to death by secret and foul means. So that the people of Iolcos murmured against Jason and his wife, and Pelias's son, Acastus, drove them out of the country, and they were forced to take refuge in Corinth.

It is sad to relate how the life of a great hero and a fearless man ended in ruin and misery, but so it was. That story shall not be told here. Instead, it is pleasanter to turn our thoughts back to the voyage of the Argonauts, to think of them speeding with sail and oar through the blue waters in search of adventure, while Orpheus plucks the strings of his harp. Even the dolphins and sea-birds listen as he sings of Heracles, of Castor and Pollux, of the great Achilles, and of Jason himself, fearless leader of the first splendid sea voyage ever made.

7

The Labours of Heracles

OF all the Greek heroes the most celebrated was Heracles, whose fame was spread throughout the ancient world. He was noted for his strength, his courage and endurance. He was the son of Zeus and his mother was Alcmene of Thebes. The goddess Hera, wife of Zeus, hated Heracles and declared war upon him from his birth. When he was no more than a baby, she sent two serpents to destroy him as he lay in his cradle; but so great was his strength that he strangled them with his infant hands. When the boy grew up, he was instructed in all the arts becoming to a hero: Eurytus, grandson of Apollo, taught him how to use the bow; Autolycus taught him wrestling; Polydeuces taught him the use of the sword and the club; from Linus he learned the art of music. But young Heracles was inclined to fits of passion, and when Linus tried to correct him, the young man killed him by striking him on the head with his own lyre.

He performed many brave deeds. One of these was to kill a lion which had been slaughtering the cattle that grazed about Thebes. For this he was acclaimed a hero throughout the country, and ever afterwards he wore the skin of this lion, with its mouth and head for a helmet. He received presents from the gods – a sword from Hermes, a bow and arrows from Apollo and a coat of golden mail from Hephaestus.

When Heracles was grown to full manhood, two women appeared before him. One advised him to live a life of pleasure, the other advised a life of glory and hardship. Heracles chose the latter. He was thus destined from youth to perform great feats of strength. Ancient writers say that he was not tall, but that his eyes sparkled with fire, and his courage was unwearying.

Soon afterwards Creon, king of Thebes, in acknowledgement of his first exploits, gave him his daughter Megara for a wife. But Hera was still the enemy of Heracles. Some years after his marriage, she set upon him a fit of madness, in which he was persuaded that Megara was his enemy. So he killed both his wife and their young children. Then, when the madness had passed, Heracles, overcome with grief and remorse, pondered how he might be purified of the crime of murdering his wife and children. He went to Delphi to consult the oracle.

An oracle is the answer given by a priest or a priestess to those who inquire what they must do. One of the most famous oracles was that of Apollo at Delphi, where the eagles circle for ever round the lofty, beetling cliff. Sometimes the oracle was of doubtful meaning, but the answer given to Heracles was clear enough. He was told to go to the city of Tiryns and serve the king, Eurystheus, who reigned from his palace in the nearby city of Mycenae. He was to remain his faithful servant for twelve years, performing all the feats which the king commanded him. These were to be ten in number. After that, if he survived, he would become immortal, sharing with the gods the privilege of everlasting life.

To the west of Mycenae lay the mountain valley of Nemea. It was ravaged by a fierce lion, so that the inhabitants had fled and taken their flocks and herds elsewhere. The first labour which Eurystheus ordered Heracles to perform was to slay the Nemean lion, and bring him back its skin. Heracles set off with the bow and arrows given to him by Apollo, and on the way he chipped for himself a stout holly club. By the time he reached the village of Cleonae, the sun had set, so he decided to rest for the night before going on into the valley. He was offered food and shelter by Molorchus, a poor cottager, who was about to make a sacrifice to Zeus.

'Stay, my friend,' said Heracles. 'Tomorrow I set off to kill the terrible lion of Nemea. Put off your sacrifice for thirty days. If by that time I return victorious, we will make a sacrifice to Zeus together. If not, then make a sacrifice to me, for I shall have died a hero's death.'

Molorchus consented, and in the morning Heracles took up his bow and arrows and his club; then, bidding the poor cottager farewell, he began the last stage of his journey to Nemea. Molorchus wished him good fortune and returned to his humble tasks. Thirty days passed and still the brave young man had not come back. With a sad heart Molorchus prepared to slay a kid and sacrifice it to Heracles. Then a passing

breeze from the direction of the Nemean valley brought to his ear the sound of footsteps on the stony track. Within a few minutes Heracles was striding towards him, bearing over his shoulder a great tawny hide. The club which he swung at his side was stained with blood.

'Come, my friend,' said Heracles, 'let us make our sacrifice to Zeus, for I have slain the terror of Nemea!'

On discovering the lion prowling about the valley, Heracles had attacked it with his arrows; but so thick and hard was the lion's skin that they fell harmlessly to the ground. Courageously the young man had closed in and aimed a savage blow at the beast with his club. Stunned by the blow, but by no means knocked out, the lion slunk into its cave. Quickly Heracles collected stones and bushes and blocked the mouth of the cave. Then he hurried to the other end and boldly entered. He at once sought out the lion and flung himself at its throat, strangling it with his bare hands, as he had strangled the serpents when he was an infant. Then, stripping off the skin, he left the carcass to the vultures and returned the way he had come.

Molorchus was amazed by this tale and saw at once that he had indeed been entertaining a hero. Together they made their sacrifice to the chief of the gods and had supper, the best that the poor man could provide.

When Heracles returned to Mycenae and presented his trophy to Eurystheus, the cowardly king fled in terror, not at the sight of the skin, but from fear of the hero's prodigious strength. He ordered Heracles in future to give the account of his exploits outside the city gates. But when he had recovered from his shock at the return of Heracles, Eurystheus insisted on wearing the lion's skin, so as to appear braver than he was.

The next task Eurystheus gave to Heracles was perhaps even more formidable. This was to slay a terrible water-serpent

called the Hydra, which ravaged the country of Argos, poisoning all whom it attacked with one of its nine heads, for its body was full of a deadly poison. Heracles took with him upon this expedition his faithful servant, Iolaus, and together they went to a cave sacred to the god Pan, where rose the spring of Amymone. It had been named after a nymph beloved of the sea god, Poseidon. The country had been suffering from drought, and in order to save the shepherds and their herds, Amymone had begged the god to allow her to touch the rock with his three-headed spear, his trident. Instantly a three-fold stream gushed from the rock, whence it flowed ever afterwards, making the country some of the greenest and most fertile in all Greece. But as the river flowed towards the sea, its bed widened, and the stream became shallower until it turned the valley into a broad marsh infested with poisonous snakes and stinging insects. Here dwelt the nine-headed Hydra, feared by man and beast for miles around. This loathsome creature was almost indestructible, for if some bold youth succeeded in cutting off one of its heads, two others appeared in its place; thus by the time Heracles came upon it, it already had many more than the nine given to it at birth.

Wading cautiously through the poisonous marshes, Heracles and Iolaus soon reached the place where the monster splashed and writhed in the water. Heracles attacked it with sword and arrow, but his efforts were in vain. No sooner did he manage to lop off one of Hydra's heads than two others took its place, each with its forked tongue spitting poison and hissing spitefully at its attacker. It was clear to the hero that some other way must be found to destroy it, so he ordered Iolaus to make a fire. This was done, though with some difficulty, on a stretch of ground which rose a little above the black waters of the marsh. Heracles then ordered Iolaus to bring red-hot spears, and with these he burnt the places where the monster's heads had been. This proved successful, for where the flesh of the creature was burnt, no new heads grew. In this way, by a mighty effort, Heracles slew the Hydra and took its loathsome body back to Mycenae.

Eurystheus was not grateful, declaring that Heracles had sacrificed all claim to recognition of this deed by taking with him a helper, Iolaus.

Artemis was a huntress and the goddess of the chase. A nymph who was being pursued by Zeus had once been saved by her, and in return the nymph had presented the goddess with a stag. This noble animal, adorned with golden antlers and hooves of brass, was the swiftest of its breed. Being sacred to Artemis, it enjoyed her protection and roamed the vales and woods unmolested.

Eurystheus ordered Heracles to bring back this stag to Mycenae.

This third labour promised to be as troublesome as the former two, but Heracles set out with a stout heart. For a whole year he pursued the animal relentlessly, scarcely stopping to rest at night. Sometimes he caught sight of its golden antlers, sometimes he glimpsed the brazen hooves as they sped up a far hillside. But he was unable to come within reach of it. As the months passed, however, the poor stag felt its strength fail, so that at last it dropped wearily to the ground, almost at the feet of its pursuer. At once Heracles tied its hind legs together, and then its forelegs, with stout cords. The panting beast was helpless and could make no resistance, as the hero hoisted it upon his back and set off in the direction of Mycenae.

He had not travelled far when he became aware of a shining presence, and the figure of a tall, graceful woman with a bow and a quiver of arrows stood before him. It was the goddess Artemis.

'How dare you,' she demanded angrily, 'seize a creature sacred to me, the goddess Artemis, and to me alone?'

Heracles laid the stag reverently at her feet and himself went down upon his knees.

'O goddess,' he began, 'huntress and protector of the hunted, I have captured this stag, not by my own will, though with great hardship, but at the will of your brother, Apollo. He it was who told me by the mouth of his oracle at Delphi to obey my taskmaster, King Eurystheus of Mycenae.'

Hearing this, the goddess graciously consented to the hero's taking the stag back to Mycenae on condition that it came to no harm and was afterwards released in its native hills. Eagerly Heracles agreed, and the goddess departed. He was faithful to his promise. As soon as Eurystheus had admired the sacred animal, Heracles returned with it to its own country and cut its bonds. Shaking the stiffness from its

limbs, the stag raised its head, sniffed the air and made off towards a familiar pool. The last Heracles saw of the graceful creature was the flash of its antlers in the distance and the gleam of its fleet hooves.

Heracles' fourth task was to capture alive yet another wild animal, the gigantic boar of Mount Erymanthus. It had descended from the mountain and was spreading terror among the dwellers in the plain. On his way to Erymanthus, armed with his club, his bow and a quiverful of poisoned arrows, Heracles encountered the Centaurs. These were the fabulous creatures with the bodies of horses and the heads and shoulders of men. Heracles shared some of their oldest wine with one of their number, Pholus. Other Centaurs, smelling the rich liquor, arrived to claim a share of it. They became quarrelsome, words and kicks were exchanged, and Heracles had to defend his life by laying about him with his great club. Their attacks grew fiercer, until he was forced to make use of the poisoned arrows, from which some of the Centaurs suffered a painful death. Some fled for refuge into the cave of the venerable Chiron, who had been the friend and tutor of many of the heroes, among them Heracles himself. Chiron was accidently wounded by a poisoned arrow. He was in such pain that he prayed for death; and when shortly afterwards it came, Heracles bitterly mourned the fate of the aged Centaur.

With a heavy heart he went on his way towards Mount Erymanthus. In the foothills he encountered the famous boar, making towards the higher slopes. Heracles drove it up into the snow, where the animal's short legs found the going difficult. Snorting and squealing, it struggled on, with Heracles gaining ground every minute. At last the beast plunged into a snowdrift, and Heracles threw over it the net he had brought for the purpose. Despite its frantic attempts to break loose, it became increasingly caught up in the meshes, so that Heracles had little difficulty in trussing it up and bearing it back to Mycenae on his broad shoulders. Some writers say that when Eurystheus caught sight of the monster's bristling hide and savage tusks, he was so terrified that he ran for safety into a brazen cell he had built for use in times of danger.

Augeas, King of Elis, was exceedingly rich in flocks and herds. His cattle, to the number of several thousand, were kept in huge stables, but the stables had never been cleaned out. The cows and horses stood knee-deep in dung, and the stench offended the noses of all who came within half a mile. Eurystheus, determined to set Heracles a task which not even he could perform, ordered him to go and clean out these stables in one day.

So Heracles set off for Elis and presented himself at the palace of the king. He undertook to clean out the stables thoroughly in one day, if Augeas would give him a piece of land in return. Augeas readily agreed; he was certain that no one could perform such a task, so that he had nothing to lose by Heracles' offer.

Accompanied by the king's son, Phyleus, as a witness, Heracles strode manfully towards the stables. Their smell told him the way. Gasping for breath, he considered what to do.

Not far from the stables flowed two rivers, the Alpheus and the Peneus. Climbing to a convenient spot in the hills where their courses turned sharply away from where the stables stood, Heracles moved a number of huge boulders, until the courses of the rivers were changed. Before long nearly all the waters of both rivers were flowing right through the Augean stables. Then Heracles and Phyleus stood back and watched the strong, fierce streams rushing through the filthy sheds. Gradually the dung that had been heaped up through the years was washed away to the sea, and before the end of the day the stables were fresh and clean. The odious stench had been blown away.

Eagerly Heracles went to the palace of the king and asked for his reward. After inspecting the stables, Augeas agreed that they had been thoroughly cleaned out in less than a day, but refused to grant Heracles his reward because, he said, the task had been done, not by the hero himself but by a trick. Indignantly Phyleus took the side of Heracles, and his father banished him from the kingdom.

After returning with the young prince to Mycenae to announce his success to Eurystheus, Heracles gathered an army and marched against Elis. After fierce fighting King Augeas was killed, and Heracles gave the throne to Phyleus. Phyleus at once granted him the piece of land his father had promised. It was this piece of land which, by the wish of Heracles, was used to hold the Olympian games, and from that time on the young men of Greece strove with each other in friendly rivalry – running, leaping, wrestling and throwing the discus.

Heracles' next task was to destroy a brood of greedy and

destructive birds. They had wings, beaks and claws of brass, and flew about the country in innumerable flocks, using their feathers as arrows and pouncing upon small, defenceless creatures. They even attacked human beings and devoured their flesh. They would descend in flocks upon the fields and make it impossible to graze sheep and plant crops in springtime. The only creatures savage enough to attack them were the wolves, and from fear of these the birds had made themselves a home on a reedy island in Lake Stymphalus in Arcadia. Eurystheus ordered Heracles to destroy them.

Faced with this task, the hero prayed to the goddess Athene, daughter of Zeus. In answer she presented him with a rattle of brass which, when twirled in the air, made a deafening noise. Standing on the bank of the lake, Heracles flourished the rattle, which startled the creatures in their hiding-place. As they rose in the air, he shot many of them with his poisoned arrows. But some of them escaped and fled far away, to cause death and destruction in another country.

The seventh labour imposed on Heracles by his cruel and

cowardly taskmaster was to bring back alive a wild beast which roamed the island of Crete. This was the beautiful white bull which the sea-god Poseidon had driven over the sea with the command to Minos, King of Crete, that he make a sacrifice of it. Unwilling to destroy so fine a creature, Minos had kept the white bull and sacrificed another. Angered by the king's deception, Poseidon drove the white bull mad and caused it to roam the island, spreading terror and destruction.

This was the beast which Heracles was ordered to bring back alive to Mycenae. King Minos was only too pleased to be rid of it. The hero sought it out, grappled with it single-handed and overcame it. Then he tied together its forefeet and its hindfeet, slung it on his back and carried it home to Mycenae. Eurystheus was so terrified at the appearance of the hero and his captive that he fled to the innermost recesses of his palace.

Heracles' eighth task was once more to overcome a breed of destructive animals. Diomedes, king of Thrace, fed his mares on human flesh, and this so inflamed them that they had no appetite for any other food. Heracles was told to bring them to Mycenae. He took with him a number of followers, among them his friend Abderus. They attacked the keepers of the mares and loosed the animals from their stables. Then Heracles and his followers drove them down to the sea coast, but the alarm had been given, and Diomedes and his men pursued the men of Mycenae. There was a battle by the sea shore, and while it was being fought, Heracles left Abderus in charge of the mares. They turned on him, kicked him to death and devoured his body. Meanwhile, in the battle, Heracles and his followers defeated the men of Thrace. Diomedes was killed and his body thrown to the horses. So he was served as he had served others.

After eating the body of their master the mares grew tame,

so that Heracles and his men had no difficulty in leading them back to Mycenae. But before leaving, the hero founded a town at the place where the battle had been fought. He named it Abdera, in memory of the friend he had lost there.

Terrified of the mares, tame though they were by this time, the cowardly Eurystheus had them sent to Mount Olympus as an offering to the gods. Zeus, however, had no wish to harbour a breed of animals reared on the flesh of men, so he had them set free on the rocky slopes of the mountain. Here they were killed and eaten by wolves and lions.

Heracles' ninth task was to get possession of a treasure desired by Eurysteus's daughter, Admete. This was a famous girdle worn by Hippolyta, Queen of the Amazons. The Amazons were women warriors, extremely fierce in battle, and had won for themselves a number of cities in the region of the Black Sea. Only their girl children were reared: all boys were either killed or sent to other places.

Heracles, accompanied by a band of followers, accordingly sailed to the country of the Amazons. When he arrived at the port of Thermodon, he was graciously received by Hippolyta, who invited him and his followers to stay for a while in her country. She promised him that when he left, she would give him the girdle as a keepsake. But the goddess Hera, enemy of Heracles, was still at work. Disguising herself as an Amazon, she spread the rumour that Heracles and his friends had come to carry off their queen. A strong band of warriors was accordingly sent to rescue Hippolyta, and Heracles, thinking she had betrayed him, and that he was in danger, killed her and seized the girdle. He and his followers then set sail with the utmost speed and made for Mycenae, bearing to Admete the prize she longed for.

On the island of Erytheia, far away to the west of Greece, near the utmost end of the Mediterranean, lived the giant

Geryon, a monster with three bodies. Geryon kept a herd of cattle which were guarded by another giant, Eurytion, and a two-headed dog called Orthrus. Heracles was commanded by Eurystheus to fetch back the oxen of Geryon. This must have seemed an impossible task, since the island of Erytheia lay at the farthest end of the known world. But Heracles travelled through many lands, until at last he came to the north coast of Africa. Making his way along this burning shore, he reached what are now called the Straits of Gibraltar at the southernmost tip of Spain. Here he set up two great rocks known as Calpe and Abila, one on each side of the strait. Some say that he made the two great rocks by splitting a larger one in half. From that time onwards these rocks have been known as the Pillars of Heracles.

So enraged was Heracles by the heat of the sun in this burning zone that he drew his bow and shot a volley of arrows at Helios, the sun god. Helios took pity on him and sent him a golden boat in which he was carried out into the Atlantic Ocean to the island of Erytheia. With keen eye and determined step the hero ranged the island until he found the famous oxen of Geryon, guarded by the mighty Eurytion. He challenged the herdsman to yield up the oxen, but Eurytion defied him and a combat took place. Heracles was attacked not only by Eurytion but also by Orthrus, his fierce two-headed dog. In the end, however, he succeeded in slaying both, just as their master, Geryon, came on the scene. Angrily he demanded to know why Heracles had slain his herdsman. For answer the hero struck the giant with all his force, first on one of his bodies, then on the other two. With a great groan Geryon sank to the ground, dead.

Heracles then drove the cattle eastwards towards his own country. To tell how he ferried them across the sea and drove them over the hills and valleys, through woods and over streams till he came once more within sight of Greece – all this would take too long. One of his hardest exploits on the journey home took place when, on reaching Thrace, Hera, his old enemy, sent his herd of oxen mad, so that they ran wildly down to the banks of the river Strymon. Here Heracles built a path across the water by dragging great blocks of stone to the water's edge and hurling them in. So the cattle passed safely across. At last he succeeded in bringing back the oxen to Eurystheus, whose only thanks were to sacrifice the whole herd to Hera.

It took Heracles eight years and one month to perform these ten labours. He now claimed his freedom, but Eurystheus still kept him as his servant. Claiming that two of the tasks had been performed unlawfully, he made him perform two more.

The first of these two added labours was to bring back some of the golden apples of the Hesperides. This task was especially difficult, since no one except the gods knew exactly where the apples grew. They hung in an orchard on Mount Atlas, beyond the place where stood the Pillars of Heracles. They were tended by three maidens called the Hesperides, or daughters of the sunset, and by the dragon Ladon, whose coils were wound day and night about the trunk of the tree from whose branches hung the apples.

After he had wandered through many lands, Heracles prayed to the goddess Athene to help him. She and her nymphs told him he must ask the old man of the sea, Nereus, who knew everything, past, present and to come.

'He will tell you where to find the golden apples,' said Athene, 'but he is difficult to approach. He will turn into water or fire or some wild beast rather than answer your questions. But do not give up hope. Be brave; hold on to him, whatever happens, and in the end you will succeed.'

So Heracles went down to the sea and there, basking on the golden sands, asleep among his daughters, the Nereids, lay the ancient god.

At the sight of Heracles the Nereids fled into the water, but the hero managed to lay hands on Nereus as he was rousing himself to see what had alarmed them. On feeling Heracles' firm grasp, he instantly became a stream of water. Heracles held on to him as tightly as he could, and then Nereus became a great fiery flame. Undaunted, Heracles still clung on, remembering the words of Athene. Next the old man became a raging lion. Just as the hero seemed about to strangle the beast to death, Nereus gave up the struggle and once more took on his original form. Heracles then demanded what he wanted to know, and Nereus told him where grew the apples of the Hesperides.

A long and arduous journey lay before the hero, but manfully he strode across deserts, over rocky places and low marshlands, through burning heat and icy cold. At length he came to the place where the giant Atlas was condemned to hold up the skies upon his shoulders. Heracles told him that it was the will of the gods that he should bring back to his master some of the golden apples from the orchard of the Hesperides.

'It will be best for you to fetch them for me,' he said. 'For the Hesperides are your daughters and will obey you. The dragon, too, will answer to your will.'

'I will do so,' thundered the giant, 'if you will perform my labour while I am gone. Can you, a mere mortal man, take upon your shoulders the burden of the skies?'

For answer Heracles bent himself to the task, and Atlas was free to go and fetch the apples. When he came back, he offered to take the apples himself to Eurystheus. But Heracles told him it was the will of the gods that Atlas should hold up the skies, while he, Heracles, returned to Mycenae. Reluctantly, therefore, Atlas resumed his burden and gave up the golden fruit to Heracles.

Once more the hero made the long journey from one end of the Mediterranean almost to the other, and so was able to give his master what he had commanded should be brought.

Heracles' twelfth and last task was the crown of all his labours. If it was not the hardest, it was the most daunting, for it meant a journey down to the kingdom of the dead to bring back the grim, three-headed watchdog Cerberus. But Heracles was not to be daunted, even by such an adventure as this. Accompanied by Athene and Hermes, the messenger of the gods, he descended by dark and narrow ways to the grey wilderness and the gloomy shades presided over by Hades and his queen Persephone. He passed through the ranks of the dead, who stretched forth their hands towards him, as if imploring his aid. Orpheus he saw, and his wife Eurydice; Sisyphus, Tantalus, and all the other wrongdoers condemned to eternal punishment. He saw also the Fates, who hold in their hands the threads of human life, and the Furies, screaming for vengeance on murderers. All these he passed by, continuing on his way unmoved until he came to the throne of the king and queen. Boldly and clearly Heracles told them why he had come. They replied that he might take Cerberus with him to the upper world on condition that he used no weapon to capture him, but only his bare hands. He must himself bring back the monster to the underworld. Heracles gave the undertaking, saluted the king and queen, and made his way back to the gates of the kingdom. Here the watchdog crouched, its six eyes baleful, its three mouths snarling and snapping with terrible menace. As the hero strode up to it, it rose on its feet and prepared to attack him. But Heracles did not flinch. In a grip of iron he seized the dog by two of its three necks and overpowered it. Seeing that Heracles was master, Cerberus made no further resistance and was carried up into the world of men; but it was unable to bear the strong light of day and spat venomously. Some said that from the place where the spittle fell sprang up the poisonous-leaved aconite.

There is little more to tell. It was believed that when Heracles reached Mycenae, his taskmaster Eurystheus was thrown into such abject terror that he immediately fled to another city, thankful to have seen the last of the hero on whom he had imposed so many formidable labours.

Nothing remained for Heracles to do except to make a second journey to the underworld and restore the watchdog to its masters. When he had done this, he left the gloomy region and regained the upper world. He never again visited the kingdom of death for, after more exploits in many lands, he became immortal, and took his place among the gods on Mount Olympus. Thus were his labours ended, and the destiny fulfilled that had been promised him by the oracle of Apollo on the cliffs at Delphi, over which the eagles wheel and scream perpetually.

8

Apollo and Daphne

THERE is a tree known as Daphne, a kind of laurel with dark green pointed leaves and small pink or white flowers which bear bright red berries. It takes its name from a Greek maiden, the daughter of the god of the River Peneus. Daphne was a girl of extraordinary beauty – beauty to excite love in the heart even of a god. But she had no interest in men or in love and marriage. She loved only hunting and the wildlife of the woods and streams. She was a follower of the chaste goddess Artemis, huntress and protector of maidens. She asked her father Peneus never to give her away in marriage – she preferred to remain as she was, free and wife to no man.

'If that is your wish, my daughter,' said her father, 'it shall be so. Yet because of your beauty, men will always follow you.'

But her first and last lover was no man: he was a god – none other than Apollo himself. It came about like this.

Eros, son of the goddess of love, Aphrodite, was playing with his bow and arrows on Mount Parnassus, home of the gods. This was the bow with which, sometimes in malice, sometimes in kindness, he shoots at gods and men and makes them fall in love, whether they want to or not. Apollo watched him.

'Mischievous boy,' he said to Eros, 'leave alone those weapons of war. They are not for you to play with. Leave bows and arrows to me. I am a mighty warrior. You are only a child.'

This angered Eros.

'With your arrows,' he replied, 'you may kill or wound anyone in the world. With my arrows I shall wound you.'

So saying, he took his bow in hand and from his quiver he drew out two arrows. One was tipped with gold and caused anyone wounded by it to fall in love with the first creature he saw. The other was blunt and tipped with lead. It made anyone it hit hate the idea of love and try at all costs to escape from it. With the leaden arrow he struck the maiden Daphne. More than ever she hated the idea of love and fled from the sight of men. Though many pursued her and asked for her hand in marriage, she refused them all. Then, standing upon a rocky pinnacle of Parnassus, he aimed the golden shaft at Apollo. It pierced him through the heart.

One day, as Daphne was striding through a wooded valley, the god Apollo caught sight of her. Newly pierced by the golden arrow of Eros, he instantly fell in love with her. He was young, and she was his first love. As soon as he approached her, she began to walk faster. As he got nearer, she broke into a run.

'Maiden,' cried Apollo, 'do not run so fast. Stop and talk to me. I have much to say.'

But Daphne only quickened her pace. The god pursued her, but so swift of foot was she that he scarcely gained upon her.

'Stop, daughter of Peneus,' Apollo pleaded, almost out of breath with running. 'I am not your enemy. You run from me as if I were a hawk and you a dove, as if I were a wolf and you a lamb. I am no hawk, I am no wolf. I shall not eat you. I love you, and I am afraid that you may fall and hurt yourself on these sharp stones. I don't wish to be cause of your injury. If you must run, run more slowly, and I will follow more slowly.'

For answer Daphne only ran the more swiftly.

'I am no countryman,' Apollo went on, 'no rude peasant. I am the son of a god – Zeus himself is my father. I am the master of Delphi and of Tenedos. I am god of music and master of the lyre. I know the secrets of nature and how to make medicines from herbs. My arrows fly truer to the mark than those of all men. But now an arrow from the bow of Eros has pierced me to the heart and I am deeply in love for the first time. For all my healing skill, I cannot cure myself of the love I feel for you. I beg you, Daphne, daughter of Peneus, stay still and let me tell you of my love.'

But Daphne ran as swiftly as ever, and Apollo scarcely gained a yard. Through groves and meadows she ran, her bright hair and loose garments streaming behind her in the fresh morning wind. Apollo's love for her grew stronger every minute as she fled before him. Urged on by the fierceness of his passion, at last he began to draw closer. He was, after all, a god, and she only a girl. How could she hope to escape him for ever? It was beyond human endurance. So she ran on, like a hare pursued by a hound – she on the wings of fear, the god following on the wings of love.

At last she felt his breath hot upon her neck. Her strength began to fail. Ready to sink to the ground, she prayed to her father, the river god.

'Peneus,' she called out with what seemed almost her last breath, 'hear your daughter and remember your promise. Let the earth open to swallow me up, or change me into some form in which I may be safe for ever from my pursuer!'

No sooner had she spoken than her prayer was answered.

Her father had heard her and recalled the promise he had made her, that she should never be wife to any man. Instantly she became fixed to the earth, as if by roots. Her body became enclosed in a soft, green bark. Her head became a tree-top and her arms branches. Out of them burst forth leaves.

Apollo stood still, overcome with amazement. Just as he seemed to be on the point of grasping the maiden he loved and had so long pursued, she became a tree – a tree with nothing of Daphne but her beauty. Apollo put his arms round the trunk and kissed the branches fervently. But all his love could not make her what she had been before.

'You will never be my wife,' he said sadly, 'but you shall for ever be my tree. I will wear your leaves as a garland round my head, and on your branches I shall hang my lyre and my bow. I have the gift of eternal youth, and you shall be ever green. Your leaves shall never wither. Let them for ever be an emblem of faithful love and unfading glory.'

The laurel bowed its head, as if in submission to the god.

9

The Gorgon's Head

1 Perseus and Danaë

IN the pleasant valley of Argos, shaded with pines and olives, reigned King Acrisius. He was a stern and hard ruler, and had offended the gods. Because of this it had been foretold that one day he would be killed by his own grandson. Under this fear Acrisius lived in Argos.

Now he had one daughter, a beautiful girl called Danaë. In order to keep her from marrying and having a son who might grow up and kill him, Acrisius locked Danaë in a brazen tower. But Zeus, the father of the gods, who cannot be cheated by the schemes of men, came to visit Danaë in her dungeon, disguising himself as a shower of golden rain. In time Danaë gave birth to a son, whom she called Perseus.

When he knew of the birth of his grandson, Acrisius was mad with rage and fear. The child must be got rid of. But he dared not further anger the gods by murdering the baby, so he took his daughter Danaë and her child down to the seashore and set them in an open boat. The poor girl's tears and the cries of the baby in her arms did nothing to soften the hard heart of Acrisius. He turned his back and strode home, leaving his daughter and his grandchild to be carried out to sea by the waves.

Danaë gave herself up for lost, certain that she and her

helpless child would be drowned in the rushing waves. But the boat bore up well, and presently she began to hope they might live. She had brought with her a little food, and with this she managed to keep herself alive and nourish the baby at her breast. Sometimes the sky was grey and overcast, and the boat drifted slowly over the water. At other times the sun shone and sparkled, and the boat danced gaily on. At night the stars came out, and at dawn the sun shone, and Danaë prayed to the gods to save her and her child. And because Danaë was good as well as beautiful and because Perseus was the son of a god, their lives were spared, and one bright morning they came in sight of the island of Seriphos.

The coast was rocky, and Danaë feared the boat might be dashed to pieces, for she had no means of keeping it off the rocks. But a fisherman named Dictys, who lived on that island by spearing or netting fish, had seen the boat and came running down to the shore. Leaning out from a rock, against which the waves broke in white spray, he flung his net over the boat and drew it in. As Danaë, with her baby in her arms, stumbled on shore, she fell upon her knees and thanked Dictys and the gods of the island for her safe coming.

Dictys was a kind man, besides being a skilful fisherman; and although he was poor, he took care of the mother and her child. Perseus grew into a strong and splendid boy, golden-haired and straight of limb. He loved to run and leap, to dive and swim, or to go off with Dictys to spear and net the fish that darted hither and thither in the sparkling water. He would play with the other boys of the island, who came to look upon him as their leader, because he could run faster, leap higher, and dive deeper than any of them.

Now the king of Seriphos was a cruel and cunning man named Polydectes. He came to hear about Danaë and the boy who had reached the island mysteriously by sea, no one knew from whence, and he sent for them to his palace. So beautiful was Danaë that he determined to marry her; but Danaë had no wish to be the wife of Polydectes, so she was continually putting him off. At length, when Perseus had grown into a tall and handsome young man, the king became jealous of him and angry that he was more loved by the people than he himself. He hated Perseus because he protected his mother, and had taken her to the temple of Athene, where she lived as a priestess so that she might not fall into the hands of Polydectes.

'I will rid myself for ever of this hateful young man,' said Polydectes to himself, frowning darkly and pulling at his black, curled beard. 'If I do not, I shall never make his mother my wife. He is beloved by the people, and perhaps he may rise against me and take my kingdom.'

Polydectes did not know that the young man was the son of Zeus and enjoyed his protection. He never suspected that the scheme by which he determined to get rid of Perseus could not succeed against the will of Zeus. His scheme was this. He gave out that he was going to marry, not Danaë, but a woman of his island called Hippodamia. In this way Perseus would think that the king had given up hope of marrying Danaë. A great feast would be held to celebrate the king's betrothal to Hippodamia, and all the best men of the island would bring gifts to show their importance and let everyone see how they honoured their ruler.

All the rich and powerful men were invited, and Polydectes took special care to see that Perseus came too, though he had nothing to bring. When the day of the betrothal came, the men of the island brought their gifts to the palace. Some brought horses or finely wrought weapons, some brought bowls of strange workmanship, or jewels, gold and woven cloths. Even the poorest brought a goat or a kid as a sign of his respect for Polydectes.

Only Perseus brought nothing. As they saw him in the king's hall with no gift, all the guests began laughing at Perseus and mocking him. Polydectes spoke to him scornfully.

'Young man,' he cried, his voice rising above the laughter of the guests, 'all my noble friends bring something, however little, to honour me on this great day. Only you have brought nothing – not even a small fish. Go back, I say, and return with some sort of gift to show that you remember who is king in Seriphos!'

Then Perseus grew angry. Blushing for shame at the laughter of the guests, and enraged at the haughty king's command, he stood up, proud and unafraid, before the whole company, his eyes blazing and his fists clenched.

'Proud king,' he said in a ringing voice, as all the guests fell silent, 'I am stronger and bolder than any other man of this country, but I have no horses, jewels and gold dishes like them, for I am poor. Nevertheless, I will go wherever you command and fetch back to you any gift you name – any gift in the world!'

'Any gift in the world?' echoed Polydectes, his eyes narrowed to cunning slits. 'Rash boy, you are an idle boaster. You had better go back to your fishing.'

'I am no boaster, and I do not lie, King Polydectes,' answered Perseus. 'I will do as I say. Name your gift, and I will fetch it, even though I must climb to the top of Mount Olympus or go down to the bottom of Hades. Whatever it is, and wherever it is, I will fetch it!'

'You are a braggart!' said Polydectes. 'Nevertheless, since you are so foolish, I order you to bring back to me the head of

Medusa, the most fearsome of the gorgons. That is the only gift I require of you.'

At this the whole company shuddered with fear, for the gorgon was one of the most horrible and deadly monsters the world had ever known.

'The gorgon's head?' cried Perseus. 'If that is your wish, King Polydectes, you shall have it. I will go at once and fetch you the gorgon's head. I depart tomorrow.'

Perseus turned on his heel and strode out of the hall, to bid farewell to his mother in the temple of Athene before setting out on his journey.

Now Medusa, whose head Perseus had promised to bring back to Seriphos, had once been one of the loveliest maidens in Greece; but she had boasted that her beauty was greater than that of Pallas Athene herself. Athene, a goddess, was angry with Medusa for this proud boast and had transformed her into a gorgon, turning her lovely face into that of a hideous monster. Her tongue lolled from her mouth, her eyes glared, her teeth became long and cruel, like the teeth of a hound, and her fair golden tresses were changed into hissing writhing snakes, which curled about her temples and terrified all who looked upon her. So terrible was her aspect that none who had ever set eyes on her remained alive. All were turned to stone at the sight of this hideous creature.

This was the monster whom Perseus had sworn to kill.

2 The Slaying of Medusa

IN the temple of Pallas Athene, Perseus prayed to the goddess. She appeared to him in a vision to instruct him before his enterprise and wish him good fortune.

'When you find the gorgon Medusa,' Athene told him, 'you must on no account look straight at her face. If you do, you will be turned to stone, like all those other luckless ones. But you may look upon her reflection, and in order that you may do so I give you this bright shield. Hold it before you, turn your back upon the gorgon, and gaze into the shield when you wish to view the monster.'

Athene handed Perseus a circular shield of brightly polished metal. In it he could clearly see his face reflected.

Then Hermes, the winged messenger of the gods, flew down from their home on Mount Olympus and addressed the young man.

'Take these winged sandals,' he said. 'With them you may fly to the ends of the earth, over land and sea.'

So Perseus took the winged sandals and strapped them on his ankles. Immediately he felt lighter, and it was with difficulty that he prevented himself from being borne aloft upon the breeze.

'You will need also three things,' the goddess told him. 'First, you must have a curved sword of great strength and hardness with which to cut off the head of Medusa. Next, you must have the magical wallet of goatskin in which to put the head when you have cut it off; and lastly you will need the helmet of invisibility. These things belong to Hades, king of the underworld. They are guarded by the Stygian maidens, who live beside the dark river which flows through the underworld.'

'How shall I find these maidens?' asked Perseus.

'Only the three grey sisters of the gorgons can tell you the way,' answered Athene. 'These sisters have only one eye between them, and this they pass from hand to hand, in order to grope their way about the far, cold lands of the north where they dwell. They have been grey-haired from birth. You must first find them, and then make them tell you where to seek the Stygian maidens and the gorgons themselves. Go now. Fly northwards, and good fortune be with you.'

Perseus thanked the goddess, and went into the temple to bid goodbye to Danaë, his mother. She wept as they parted, but he told her to have courage. Then, taking the polished shield in his right hand, he rose in the air and flew towards the cold and darkness of the far north. Over forests and hills he skimmed, past lakes and rivers, until he came to the shores of a grey, unfriendly sea. He searched here and there, gazing now at the land itself, now at the reflection of the seashore in his bright shield, and at last he made out three grey figures, bent and groping in the half-darkness of the northern night.

Perseus alighted silently behind them, and as he did so he

saw one of them pass to another a round and glittering object which she had taken from a socket in her forehead. It was the single eye.

Swiftly Perseus snatched the eye from her and greeted the crones.

'Hail, grey sisters of the gorgons,' he said. 'Tell, I bid you, where I may find your sisters and the Stygian maidens who guard the treasures of the underworld!'

'Who is this man who speaks with so loud and commanding a voice?' asked one of the women querulously. 'Give me the eye, sister, that I may see him.'

'I gave you the eye,' said the other. 'You took it from my hand even now.'

'I have your eye, grey sisters,' said Perseus. 'I shall not give it back until you have told me what I must know. Now speak!'

The grey sisters grumbled and pleaded, but there was nothing for it but to explain to Perseus how he might find the Stygian maidens and the gorgons.

As soon as he knew the way, Perseus gave back the eye to the foremost of the crones, and sped southward on his flight towards the underworld.

In time the bright-haired young man alighted on his winged sandals beside the dark and fearful stream of death, which is called Styx, and there he found the maidens. He told them he had been sent by the goddess Athene to ask for the treasures they guarded. They looked with curiosity at the tall stranger who claimed to have been sent by the goddess, but without objection they gave him the things he requested. So now Perseus had all he needed – the curved sword, the goatskin wallet, and the dark helmet of invisibility. Then they directed him to where he might find the gorgons, those dreaded monsters, one of whom turned men to stone at the mere sight of her horrific face. Perseus thanked the maidens and sped on until he came to a place where stood many grey rocks and stones weathered by rain and storms but still in the likeness of men. Amidst these, the victims of Medusa, lay the gorgons asleep.

Two of them were in the form of winged swine, tusked and hairy, but Medusa was easily distinguished. She had the form of a once beautiful girl, but her brazen claws and sharp teeth proclaimed her a monster. Beneath the frowning brows her fierce eyes were closed in sleep, but amidst her tangled locks a hundred serpents hissed and writhed. No wonder men had been turned to stone at the mere sight of so terrible a creature. Perseus, even though he saw her, not directly, but reflected in the bright shield he held aloft, shuddered at the image of Medusa. But he did not hesitate.

He had a task to perform, and he must carry it out before the monsters awoke.

Hovering over the sleeping form of Medusa, he raised his sharp, curving sword on high, and swooped. One tremendous sweeping blow, made with the young man's full strength, was enough. The head was severed at a stroke. Swiftly Perseus alighted beside the body and, still keeping his eyes turned away, raised the head by its tangled, snaky locks and thrust it into the wallet at his side. The gorgon did not wake, but a miraculous thing happened: from the drops of blood falling from her body arose the winged horse Pegasus. The beautiful white animal stretched its wings, neighed, and with a clatter of hooves took to the air and sped off towards Mount Helicon, where it became the plaything of the Muses, those maidens who inspire the artists and poets among men. With their help painters make wonderful pictures and the poets of all ages write their songs. But first they must drink from the

springs which arose amidst the snows of Mount Helicon, where Pegasus printed his hooves.

The sound of the horse awoke the two sleeping gorgon sisters, who instantly snorted and sprang into the air in pursuit of the tall stranger who had slain their sister. Over mountain and plain they followed him, but his helmet of invisibility protected him from their sight. At length the gorgons gave up their pursuit, and Perseus was able to wing his way unmolested, in search of the island of Seriphos whence he had come. The journey home was still to be accomplished, but the prize of his undertaking, the terrible head of Medusa, was safe in the magical wallet which hung at his side.

3 The Giant Atlas

AND now the journeyings of Perseus were fraught with storm and danger. First he was blown back to the far north, to the country of the Hyperboreans, near the place where he had talked with the grey sisters. Then a hurricane from the polar regions swept him far to the south, until he found himself over the burning equator. Buffeted by storms, he battled on through the air, by day and by night, saved only by the winged sandals from being dashed to pieces in the crags of a mountain-range, or drowned for ever in the stormy seas. From his place among the clouds he beheld the shores of the Baltic Sea, the Danube river, the Black Sea, the mighty Alps, and the Iberian coast where the great Atlantic breakers surge and roll. Then at last a calm and gentle breeze carried him to the country of the Hesperides, the blessed land of the west. Here the Sun's weary horses rest after they have borne his great chariot through the skies during the long, burning day.

Now the Hesperides were the daughters of evening, and they sang and played in a garden belonging to the giant Atlas. Atlas was one of the Titans, the largest creatures in human form whom the world had ever seen. In his garden was a wonderful tree, on which grew clusters of golden apples. The leaves too were of pure gold. Because he was afraid the apples might be stolen, Atlas had built a high wall about his garden. Moreover he employed the dragon Ladon to help the Hesperides to guard the golden apples.

Flying over this pleasant place, Perseus felt a great desire to rest there for the night. Evening was coming on, and he was weary after the buffeting of so many storms. So he alighted near the gate of the garden and addressed the giant Atlas,

gazing up at his huge form as it towered among the sunset clouds.

'Mighty Atlas!' the young man called. 'I crave your hospitality and shelter for the night. Have I your leave to rest my tired limbs amidst the grass in your garden?'

Like thunder the voice of the giant rolled down from on high. 'Who are you, bold youth?'

'I am Perseus, and I claim your hospitality. If it is brave deeds you honour, then give me leave to tell you of my adventures, and especially of the great feat I have just carried out with the help of Athene. Or if it is high birth that moves your heart, then know I am the son of Zeus himself, father of all the gods!'

Now Atlas did not like the sound of this. He feared the anger of Zeus, for he and his Titans had warred against the gods; and he suspected that Perseus might have been sent to steal his treasured apples.

'I care not for boasters,' he thundered, 'nor liars! I believe not a word of your tale. Be off with you. Trouble me no more. You shall not set foot in my garden!'

Perseus continued to beg for the hospitality of the giant, but Atlas stooped down and began to handle him roughly, as if to take him up in his mighty arms and cast him into the sea that beats along those shores. In vain Perseus struggled. How could he prevail against the hugest man on earth? So, almost out of breath, he made as if to retreat from the giant. Then, turning away his face, he swiftly drew the head of Medusa from its goatskin wallet and held it aloft. The eyes of the monster glared and crackled; the snakes spat and curled. And Perseus shouted in defiance:

'Then since you deny me hospitality and insult the son of a god, take the gift I bring you! Gaze your fill on this, stone-hearted Atlas!'

With a terrible groaning, like a volcano in labour, the giant was turned to stone. In the very act of becoming the great mountain which still bears his name, the Titan grew in height and bulk. His bones and sinews became stone, his beard and the hair upon his head and body turned to forests. His shoulders and arms became the upper parts of the mountain, and his back and legs the stony base that bore up the whole gigantic pile. The entire weight of the skies, with all their wheeling planets, rested upon the shoulders and head of the mountain. And so, for his insults and unkindness to a son of great Zeus, Atlas was condemned to bear for ever the weight of the universe.

Almost dropping asleep – for night had now come and the stars were bright in the western sky, and the sun's tired steeds had long disappeared over the far horizon – Perseus lay down amidst the pleasant streams of the garden of the Hesperides. He slept long and deeply, and in the morning arose and prepared to fly eastward towards his homeland. Gently he skimmed across the burning desert of Libya, until at last he found himself carried to the country of Ethiopia to the far east of the great sea. At his side still hung the magical wallet, but from it some drops of gorgon's blood escaped and fell to earth along the Libyan coast. No sooner had each of these drops sunk into the sand than it sprang up in the form of tiny serpents. These grew and increased in number, and this is the reason why the coasts of Libya have ever since been troubled with snakes, those descendants of the gorgon's blood.

4 Perseus and Andromeda

THE country of the Ethiopians was ruled by a king and queen named Cepheus and Cassiopeia. They had one daughter, Andromeda. Queen Cassiopeia had been foolish enough to say that both she and her daughter were more beautiful than the Nereids, sea-maidens in the protection of the god Poseidon. Beautiful as were the queen and her daughter, they did not compare with the Nereids, and Poseidon was justly angered by their boast. So to punish them he sent a terrible flood along the coast of Philistia, where the Ethiopians lived; and worse still, he sent a huge sea-serpent which ranged along the shore, terrorizing the people and making it impossible for the fishermen to go out in their boats. The country was threatened with ruin.

King Cepheus went and consulted the priests, and they told him that the only way he could calm the anger of the god was to sacrifice his daughter Andromeda to the sea-serpent. In vain Cepheus pleaded, but at last he gave in. Sorrowfully he and Cassiopeia had to see their daughter chained to a rock near the shore.

This is the reason why the young man Perseus flying over Egypt, across the Nile and eastwards to Philistia, beheld a beautiful maiden chained to a rock, her fair hair streaming in the wind. Tears flowed from her eyes as the cruel sea broke in foam against the ledge on which she was chained. So moved was Perseus by the helpless beauty of the girl that he at once fell in love with her. He determined to rescue her and make her his bride.

The young man flew down to the shore where Cepheus and Cassiopeia stood weeping and wringing their hands, as they gazed towards the place where their daughter must surely soon be the victim of the sea-serpent.

They told him who they were and how Andromeda had fallen into so hapless a plight.

'I will go to her rescue,' said Perseus, 'and then I shall claim her as my wife. I am a son of Zeus and have slain the gorgon, so I am well fitted to be the husband of a king's daughter.'

'Indeed, yes,' said Cepheus. 'But you must first slay the sea-serpent. Then you shall marry my daughter, and with her I will give you rich presents.'

A great cry broke from the Ethiopians gathered by the shore.

'The serpent!' they cried. 'See, the monster appears!'

They pointed to where, on the horizon, a churning and pounding of great waves betrayed the monster's presence. Without waiting for further speech, bright-haired Perseus rose into the air, clutching resolutely in his right hand the curved sword with which he had cut off the head of Medusa. Breathlessly the king, the queen and all the people watched as he skimmed over the rock where Andromeda was chained, awaiting the coming of the sea-beast. In a few moments it was clearly to be seen, the coils of its great trunk lashing the water into a snowy foam. The angry swirling of its huge tail made great whirlpools in the water, and the waves that spread towards the shore rose and smashed into splinters the little boats of the fishermen. Straight for Andromeda's rock the beast swam, plumes of white sea-water hissing from its nostrils.

Perseus approached it from behind, hovering over it like an eagle about to dive upon a helpless lamb. He fixed his eyes upon a spot just behind the serpent's scaly head and plunged straight upon it, stabbing the point of his sword into the creature's body. The serpent turned, stung by the blow, and lashed at Perseus with its tail. But the young man rose high in the air, just in time to avoid its deadly aim. Again and again Perseus struck and stabbed at the serpent until the sea was stained with its dark blood and the scarlet foam swirled and boiled upon the waves. The beast was helpless under the attacks of the hero, and at last it turned in flight. But Perseus would not allow it to escape. He pursued it with blow after blow, until with a great groaning and hissing the monster almost rose out of the water and then sank back, to disappear for ever under the troubled sea.

The crowds on the shore gave a great shout of joy at the hero's victory. Their land was free, they could fish in peace once more. Cepheus and Cassiopeia were overcome with relief and happiness. Their daughter was saved. They ran to greet their deliverer as, alighting first on the rock to unchain Andromeda, he bore her to the shore to be reunited with her parents. He at once claimed his bride, and Andromeda joyfully assented, asking that the marriage feast should be held without delay.

A magnificent banquet was prepared, and the chief subjects of King Cepheus were invited. All was joy and merriment. But just as the guests were raising their wine-cups to drink the health of the bride and her handsome bridegroom, the door of the hall burst open. An angry man, called Phineus, and a party of his friends broke rudely into the gathering, armed with spears and swords.

'This ceremony must be stopped!' cried Phineus. 'I demand the hand of Andromeda in marriage. She was promised to me, together with a rich dowry, by her parents. She is mine by right. I come to claim her.'

'Is this true?' asked Perseus in amazement.

'It is true,' answered the king. 'This man was indeed promised the hand of my daughter in wedlock. But,' he added, turning upon the angry suitor, 'you forfeited your right to her when she was chained to the rock and left as a sacrifice to the sea-serpent. If you desired her, you should have slain the monster, and saved my daughter. You are a coward, and have lost the maiden to a braver man. Perseus is her true husband.'

'Well said, King Cepheus!' cried the guests. 'Perseus is your daughter's true husband.'

For answer Phineus shouted, 'Then he shall die!' and flung his spear in the direction of his rival. But he missed his aim, and a battle followed between the friends of Phineus and some young men among the guests who favoured Perseus. Swords were flourished and spears thrown, and some were killed in the fighting. Phineus's followers outnumbered their enemies, and soon the fight began to go against Perseus. Suddenly the young man leapt upon one of the tables and cried:

'Let all who are my friends turn away their faces!'

So saying he pulled the gorgon's terrible head from its goatskin wallet and held it up.

'We are not deceived by your trickery!' shouted one of the friends of Phineus, and instantly he became a stone statue in the act of hurling his spear.

Phineus himself had taken refuge behind a pillar, and seeing that his friends were turned to stone and Perseus was victor, he covered his face and begged for mercy.

But Perseus, keeping his own eyes turned from the snaky head, jumped from the table and sprang after Phineus, forcing him to look full into the eyes of Medusa.

'Such is the mercy I show you!' said Perseus grimly. 'So you shall remain for ever, on your knees, the very statue of a coward.'

Thus ended the battle between Perseus and his rival, and thus the hero won the bride he had rescued. In thankfulness to the gods who had protected him, he raised three altars – one to Athene, one to Hermes, and one to Zeus, father of all the gods. And after he had laid offerings upon them, he began to think of bidding farewell to the father and mother of his bride, and returning to discover how his own mother had been faring. With her heart full of happiness the beautiful Andromeda prepared to go with her brave and noble husband.

5 The Return of Perseus

MEANWHILE in Seriphos, the kingdom of Polydectes, Danaë, in spite of the protection of the good fisherman Dictys, was being increasingly persecuted by the king. Polydectes was determined to marry her. She still refused, for he was a hard and cruel man. Polydectes had sent her son away on a dangerous task; indeed, he was certain that Perseus, whom he hated because of his courage and his love for his mother, would be killed in trying to get the gorgon's head. King Polydectes had had no news of the young man, so once more he spoke to Danaë.

'Your son has been slain on this foolhardy errand,' he said. 'You had better marry me and make your home here as queen in Seriphos.'

But still Danaë refused, placing herself under the protection of Dictys and of the goddess Athene.

So the amazement and anger of Polydectes can be imagined when messengers came to say that a ship had just put into harbour bearing Perseus. The king was at that very moment enjoying a feast at his palace.

'Let him come straight to me,' he commanded. 'He has brought me a love-gift, I am sure.'

So sarcastic was his tone that the guests all jeered and laughed.

'Yes, let us see the young hero,' they said. 'Let us hear how the boaster has fared who claims to be descended from Zeus.'

No sooner had Perseus landed than he went straight to the palace of the king, leaving his wife Andromeda and her servants at the temple of Athene. Alone, the fair-haired young man strode into the palace of the king, walking between rows of tall columns into the great marble banqueting-hall. He had

116

left behind his sword, his polished shield, his helmet of invisibility and the winged sandals of Hermes. He carried with him only the goatskin wallet containing the head of Medusa. He had brought it as he promised, to be a wedding present for Polydectes on his marriage to Hippodamia. He little knew that Polydectes had no intention, nor ever *had* any intention, of marrying this lady. It had been a mere pretence, to make Perseus think he no longer wished to make Danaë his wife. So Perseus was ready to give the head to the king.

As he stood before the whole assembly, looking straight across the crowded hall to where Polydectes waited to receive him, the guests admitted that he was a handsome youth, taller and stronger than ever before; his bronzed face showed the marks of travel in sun and wind, storm and conflict.

'So,' said the king, 'you have come back. Did you remember my wedding present? Or have you perhaps forgotten to slay the gorgon?'

He laughed and the guests joined in the laughter.

'No matter,' Polydectes went on. 'I have no need of any gift from you, young man, except the hand of your mother in marriage. I shall not marry the lady Hippodamia, and I can do without the gorgon's head.'

Once more the guests laughed and jeered. Then, his eyes flashing with anger, Perseus raised his voice above their jeering and clapping and said:

'Nevertheless, Polydectes, tyrant and monster that you are, here is your love-gift. You shall behold the prize of my undertaking, whether you will or not! See what I have brought you!'

Swiftly he plunged his hand into the wallet and, turning his own face from the assembly, held the fearsome object up before the eyes of all. Instantly, before he understood what was happening, Polydectes was turned to stone, his smile of contempt frozen on his bearded face. The guests too, one and all, became statues, some with cups in their hands, some with grinning lips, others with a look of fear just breaking out in their stone eyes.

So ended the cruel king of Seriphos. Perseus took command and made Dictys king in his place. Then he gave the head of Medusa into the keeping of the goddess Pallas Athene, who had been his protectress throughout his long adventure. Hermes took charge of the winged sandals, the wallet and the helmet of invisibility; being the messenger of the gods, he undertook to restore them to the keeping of the Stygian maidens in Hades.

When all this had been done, and sacrifices made to the gods, Perseus with his wife and mother set out for the kingdom of Argos, whence, as a baby, he had been driven forth on the waves by his grandfather Acrisius. Danaë had long ago told Perseus how Acrisius had been angry with her for bearing a son, and so had set them both adrift on the sea. That was many years ago, and Perseus hoped that his grandfather would by this time have forgiven them and would welcome

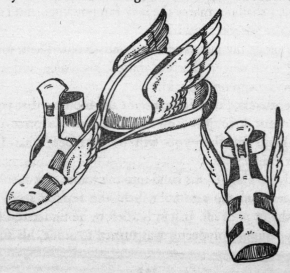

them in Argos. But Acrisius had heard that his daughter and her son were returning and, being afraid of the prophecy by which he was to be killed by his own grandson, had fled to the neighbouring city of Larissa in the country of Thessaly.

On their way home Perseus, Danaë and Andromeda stopped to rest in this very city of Larissa. Here the king was holding athletic games in honour of the gods. At these games the young men of the country ran and wrestled, leaped and threw the discus in friendly competition. Prizes were given and a great feast held to mark the end of the games. Strangers were invited to take part.

Perseus presented himself to the king of Larissa as a young man of noble blood and great exploits, and the king invited him to compete. Perseus, anxious to show his prowess before his mother and his newly married bride, at once agreed to take part in the competition to see how far he could throw the discus, a circular plate of bronze which, properly thrown, flies incredible distances through the air. Everyone watched as the young man made his first throw. It would have been a good one but, as luck would have it, and the will of the gods, a wind struck up and carried it off its course. The metal disc went wild, and Perseus was dismayed to see that it hit an old man in the ankle as he sat and watched the games. Stunned by the shock of this terrible blow, the old man fell dead to the ground. Still greater was Perseus's dismay when he learned that the old man was none other than his grandfather, Acrisius. Such was the will of the gods, and so perished Acrisius according to the prophecy. No man may escape divine justice.

Lamentation was made for the death of Acrisius, and after sacrifices had been paid to the gods of the country, Perseus left Larissa and departed for Argos with his wife and mother. Here, in the pleasant valley, shaded by pines and olives, he lived and reigned justly for many years.

10

Philemon and Baucis

ON a hill in the country of Phrygia stand two trees, an oak and a lime, so close together that their trunks are intertwined. Near them is a lake where now only the birds live. Long, long ago a flourishing city stood there. This is the story of how the city became a lake, and the two trees grew together, side by side.

One day Zeus, father of the gods, and his son Hermes travelled through Phrygia, disguising themselves as poor men, in order to see how kind the people of that country were to strangers. From door to door they went, seeking shelter for the night, but not a door was opened to them. The richer the houses, the meaner was their reception.

'It is too late,' the voices said from behind barred doors. 'Be on your way. We have no room for strangers.'

'It is near nightfall,' another voice would say. 'Be off with you. We want no tramps and beggars here.'

Zeus and Hermes trudged on. At last, just as they were at the point of despair, they found a tiny thatched cottage on the outskirts of the city, whose door was opened at their knock. It was the home of two old people, Philemon and his wife Baucis. They were very poor, but managed to make ends meet by thrift and the kindness of their hearts. In the houses of the rich you will find masters and servants. In the cottage of Philemon and Baucis there was no master and no servant. Both were masters and both served each other.

As soon as the two gods bent their heads to enter the low doorway, the old man brought forward a bench for them to rest on, and his wife threw upon it an old rug made of sheepskin, worn and tattered with age. Then Baucis raked out the ashes of the fire and threw on dried leaves and bark. Bending low before the fire, she blew upon it and kindled the dying embers into flames. She threw some sticks on the fire and put on an old cooking pot full of water. Philemon brought in vegetables and herbs from the garden, and Baucis cut them up and put them in the pot. The old man took down a side of smoked ham from the beam above the chimney, cut off slices of the meat and put them in the pot with the herbs and vegetables. Then, while the meal was heating, Philemon gave his guests a bowl of water to wash in, asking them politely about their journey and the road they had come by.

Next Baucis, with trembling hands, placed a rickety table before the travellers, wiped its worn surface with sweet-smelling herbs and placed upon it some olives in a wooden bowl. Beside this she laid some cheese and a salad in dishes of cracked earthenware, the best she had in her cupboard. Then she found wooden cups and a pitcher of clear water. Her husband brought out a little wine, which he poured into a bowl for the entertainment of the travellers. The steaming dish of meat and vegetables was soon ready, and this was put on the table. Baucis, in her ancient, trembling voice, bade the guests welcome, and urged them to eat and drink.

Zeus and Hermes, delighted with their welcome, began to eat of the food and drink of the wine and water, while Philemon and Baucis chatted to them of this and that, stopping from time to time to put more sticks on the fire or serve them with cheese and salad. As the meal went on, the old folks were disturbed to see that, as soon as the wine bowl began to be emptied, it was refilled as if by magic. There had been little enough wine to start with, but now it seemed as if there was a never-ending stream. It was this which made Philemon and Baucis realize that they were entertaining gods. How else was the endless supply of wine to be explained? Looking into the faces of their guests, they could now see that they were indeed no mere men, but immortals from heaven. So they fell upon their knees before Zeus and Hermes and begged them to grant pardon for their humble entertainment.

Then the old couple put their heads together and considered how they might offer something worthier of their divine guests. Waddling about the doorway of their cottage was a goose, ancient but stately, which they kept as a guardian of their household. It had at least enough strength to cackle when danger approached. They made up their minds to sacrifice the goose in honour of their guests. They would capture it, wring its neck, pluck it and get it ready for the pot. This at least would be better than the smoked ham and vegetables which was the best they had been able to offer.

But the goose refused to have anything to do with the old people's plan. It fled from them, ran round the cottage,

squawling indignantly, and finally sheltered on the floor between the feet of the gods. Zeus forbade the old people to kill it, saying:

'Spare the goose, my friends, guardian of your household. You have feasted us well, and we have no need of it. We are gods, and everywhere but in your cottage we have been treated with meanness and inhospitality. We must repay the inhabitants of this land as they have served us, but we will protect you. Leave your house and come with us to the top of that hill. Do as we bid.'

The gods arose from their bench and led the way up the hill. Philemon and Baucis obeyed. Each with a staff in hand, they hobbled and panted up the hill behind their guests. It was now night, but the sky was bright with stars. Turning round, they saw by the light of the stars that a great water had risen and covered all the city behind them, except only their tiny cottage. It alone was left standing above the flood. The old couple, breathing hard after their efforts to climb the hill, gazed upon the scene, wringing their hands and lamenting the fate of their neighbours, whose houses had been swallowed up in the rising water. Then they saw a marvel. For their cottage was transformed by divine magic into a temple. Its creaking posts and weathered walls were turned into columns of stone. Its thatched roof became pure gold. Its floor was paved with marble.

Zeus spoke kindly to the old couple.

'You have given the gods a welcome where others barred their doors,' he said. 'We have saved you from destruction, and your cottage has been turned into a temple fit for the worship of the gods. What request will you make us? Whatever you desire shall be granted you.'

Philemon and Baucis mumbled together. It did not take them long to make up their minds.

'We ask,' said Philemon in his old, quavering voice, 'to be allowed to spend the rest of our lives as guardians of the temple that was our home. Here we have lived, and here we will die together when our time comes. We wish to be allowed to die at the same moment, so that my wife may not live to see my funeral nor I ever behold her grave.'

Their request was granted. For the rest of their lives they were the priests of the temple, keeping it clean and accepting the sacrifices of pious travellers, sweeping its floor and setting fresh herbs upon the altar.

Then one day, when they were very old indeed, they stood together before the temple. As they talked quietly together of old times, a chill wind blew. They both shivered, and Baucis saw Philemon begin to grow leaves. Philemon saw his wife changing in the same way. They felt themselves rooted to the ground. Leaves grew about their heads, and they soon knew that they were becoming trees. They bade farewell to each other, but neither felt sad. They had lived long and were tired. They had been together as long as they could remember, and even death was not to separate them. Bark had grown up around their old limbs.

'Goodbye, dear wife,' said Philemon.

'Goodbye, my husband,' sighed Baucis with her last breath, and the bark closed silently over their mouths.

The man had become an oak, and the woman a lime tree.

For many years the Phrygian shepherds showed the two trees to their children and grandchildren, telling them the story of the old people whose kindness to strangers had earned them the reward of being together for ever. As the years went by, they grew closer even than they had been in life. Their trunks and their boughs were twisted together, so that it was hard to say which was which.

11

Eros and Psyche

PSYCHE was the youngest daughter of a king and queen. Her two elder sisters were more than commonly beautiful, but Psyche's loveliness was such that strangers drew in their breath when they saw her. She was slender and graceful; her hair hung in soft coils about her shoulders; her gestures and movements, her voice and her smile, were full of charm and sweetness. But it was the beauty of her face, above all, which attracted every gazer. The blue depths of her eyes, despite a certain mournfulness, seemed to smile with a faraway look, as if she were dreaming of things outside this world. So great was the fame of Psyche's beauty that people came from distant lands only to look at her. They said she was lovelier even than Aphrodite herself, queen and goddess of beauty.

Gradually men began to forsake the altars of Aphrodite and pay devotion only to Psyche. They strewed flowers in her path and offered up prayers to the young princess. When the news of this reached Aphrodite, she was incensed with anger. What was the use of having been proclaimed goddess of beauty if a mere mortal was to be worshipped as if she were divine?

'I will be revenged on this impudent girl,' she cried. 'I will make her sorry for her extraordinary powers of attraction.'

The son of Aphrodite was a young man of unusual beauty named Eros. In some regions he was worshipped as the god of love, though indeed it was Aphrodite herself who should have been so regarded. Eros roamed the earth with a bow and a quiver full of arrows, and if he aimed at a mortal in the presence of another of the opposite sex, instantly his victim fell in love. Sometimes Eros was regarded as being blindfolded, so that his arrows fell haphazardly. If he were nearby, any man or woman might instantly fall in love with anyone else, for no apparent reason whatsoever. Sometimes Eros used his power with kindliness and foresight; sometimes blindly and for sheer mischief.

In her anger against poor Psyche, Aphrodite sent for her son.

'Go and find that wretched young woman,' she told him, 'and make her fall in love with some hideous creature. In this way she will be punished for her presumption.'

In the garden of Aphrodite were two fountains, one of sweet water, the other of bitter. Eros took from each a tiny bottle and with these he hastened to Psyche's room in her father's palace. Here he found her asleep, and from the bottle of bitter water he sprinkled a few drops on her lips. At once Psyche awoke and opened her eyes. Eros was invisible. But in that instant he fell in love with her, so overcome was he by her beauty. He was full of sorrow at what he had done, and tried to undo it by sprinkling her hair with the sweet water from the other bottle. Thus Psyche felt both joy and bitterness, delighting in her beauty but sorrowing because it seemed to make all men afraid of her. For Aphrodite, goddess of love, was her enemy and her beauty brought her no happiness. Everyone admired her; everyone spoke her praises; but no prince nor king nor commoner sought her hand in marriage. They were afraid to court one whom all united in worshipping. It was as if she were above even kings. Her two sisters, more moderate in charms, had both found husbands among neighbouring princes; but Psyche alone sat brooding in her room, hating the very perfection of beauty which brought her only flattery but no love.

The girl's unhappy state alarmed her father and mother. They feared they had in some way offended against the gods, so they sought the advice of the oracle – the answer given by a priest or priestess to those who ask what they must do. They went to see the priest of Apollo in his temple at Delphi and asked what they should do.

Sternly the oracle replied:

'Your daughter is not meant to be the wife of any mortal lover. She is destined by the gods to be the bride of a monster whom neither gods nor men can resist. He dwells upon the top of a mountain, and thither your daughter must go and seek him.'

When these terrible words were known, all the people were horrified. Some wept and some tore their hair. The king and queen were almost out of their minds. But poor Psyche took the news more calmly.

'My dear parents,' she said quietly, 'you grieve now; yet before, when the people greeted me as a goddess, you rejoiced. You should have grieved then, and so you would have been ready for this cruel oracle. I am resigned to my fate. Lead me to it.'

So a procession wound slowly up the pine-covered slopes of the mountain, and on the top of it Psyche was left alone.

For a long time the princess stood on the summit of the mountain. Chill winds blowing across the stony wastes made her gather her robe tightly about her. She began to feel afraid, and tears filled her eyes.

'What have I done to deserve such a fate as this?' she asked herself in anguish. 'Was it my fault that all men called me beautiful and foresook the altars of Aphrodite?'

Then, as if in answer to her words of sorrow, the wind changed, and Zephyrus, blowing strong and warm from the west, lifted the girl in his arms and carried her gently down the mountain into a flowery vale, full of sweet perfumes and the murmur of birds among the summer leaves. Here Psyche lay down beside a rippling stream and fell fast asleep.

When she awoke, she found herself near a grove of stately trees surrounding a pleasant spring of pure water. Into this grove she strayed, and before long she was standing in front of a delightful palace. It seemed to have been designed and built, not by men, but by some god. She entered the palace and wandered through its stately apartments, marvelling at the golden pillars supporting the carved roof, the elaborate paintings of gods and hunting scenes which adorned the walls. There were carvings and sculptures, jewelled objects of rare worth, and many other treasures to captivate the eye.

As she was gazing at a richly embroidered screen, Psyche was surprised to hear a voice, though no one was in sight.

'Fair queen,' said the voice, 'this palace is yours and all that it contains. We whose voices you hear are your servants, and we will obey your every command. Go to your own apartment and rest on the bed. Afterwards you will find your bath prepared, and nearby you will find a table on which will be food for your refreshment. If you will be pleased to partake of these things, we will be in attendance to see that you lack nothing.'

After she had rested and bathed, Psyche sat down to enjoy the delicious meal which appeared as if by magic. As she ate and drank, her ears were feasted on the music of hidden instruments, ravishingly sweet and harmonious. She began to forget her fears and even the fate that awaited her.

She had not yet seen her future husband – the cruel monster to whom she had been promised. But he came at night and left her before the hours of darkness had passed. She was surprised to find that he spoke to her, not in fierce and threatening tones, but only in words of love and admiration. She longed to see him, but he would not let her.

'It is better,' the gentle voice told her, 'that I should remain unseen. I beg you not to ask to see my face. I love and cherish you, dear Psyche, and I urge you to obey this request.'

'But I love you,' said Psyche, 'and I want to see you. That is natural, surely.'

'If you love me,' answered the voice, 'that is enough. I am content that you should love me as your husband. If you saw me, you might adore me, or fear me as a god. It is better that you should be content to love me and be loved by me.'

For a time Psyche was happy. She was content to leave things as her husband had ordered. Each night he came as darkness fell, and before dawn he had fled, leaving her to spend her days peacefully in the palace he had provided for her. But at last she began to think of her absent parents, grieving for her, and of her two sisters, to whom she would have liked to show all the wonders of her home. Beautiful as was this home, it began to seem to her no more than a lovely prison.

One night, when her husband was at her side, she told him of her distress, and at last he promised to let her sisters visit her. This at least would be something to make her feel less a prisoner than before. So Zephyrus, spirit of the west wind, was summoned, and next day he visited the two sisters. He led them by the hands over the mountain and down into Psyche's valley. Psyche greeted them with outstretched arms and took them into her palace. They were shown all the marvels of its golden halls, its marble baths and spacious sleeping chambers; they were attended by the invisible servants and feasted on rare and delicate dishes.

Naturally enough, they became jealous of their sister. They asked her numerous questions. Above all, they wanted to know what her husband was like. She told them that he was a beautiful young man who was at home only in the hours of darkness and spent his days hunting among the hills and vales of the surrounding country.

This answer did not satisfy the sisters, and at last they made her confess that she had never seen him.

On learning this, they began to fill Psyche's mind with doubts and suspicions. They asked her if she had forgotten the words of the oracle of Apollo, that her husband was to be a monster, feared and hated by all men.

'Mark my words,' said one of the sisters, 'he is no fair youth but a serpent who has learned the voice of man to flatter and cherish you with loving tones, the more easily to strangle and devour you when he has tired of you. No wonder he will not allow himself to be seen by the light of day!'

'I cannot believe it,' protested Psyche.

'Ah, but it is more than likely. Remember, sister, the oracle cannot lie. If you take our advice, you will protect yourself by doing as we say. When your husband is asleep, provide yourself with a lamp and a sharp knife. Take a long look at him, but before he can wake, cut off his head and so rid yourself of the monster. Then once again you will be free. You will be able to enjoy the all pleasures and treasures of your palace without fear of being devoured.'

Psyche indignantly refused to believe her sisters. She told them she would never do as they advised. Yet when they had returned to their own homes, their words remained behind to poison her thoughts. Besides, she was still curious to see her husband.

One day, therefore, overcome by suspicion and curiosity, she hid a lamp and a sharp knife in her room. That night she waited until her husband was sound asleep. Silently the girl uncovered the lamp and held it over the sleeping husband. She was amazed and overcome with joy at what she saw. It was no cruel monster but Eros himself, loveliest of the sons of gods. His manly features were relaxed in sleep, his curled locks strayed over his shoulders, behind which grew his two soft, white-feathered wings – the wings on which he flies here and there upon the earth, causing joy and distress among men and girls as he aims his arrows at their hearts. So this was the monster who had been destined as Psyche's husband. Certainly all men feared and some hated him; certainly he seemed cruel to many. But to Psyche he was her perfect husband and lover.

In her joy and amazement she leaned closer over the sleeping form of Eros, and burning oil fell from the lamp on to his shoulder. Instantly the god was awakened by the stinging pain of the burns. He saw Psyche with the gleaming knife in her hand. She had forgotten it in the moment of her joy. Without a word Eros rose from the bed, spread his snowy wings and flew from the window. Psyche, with no thought but to follow her husband, leaped through the window after him and fell to the ground. Eros turned in his flight and spoke to her.

'Oh, Psyche,' he said, 'how foolish of you to mistrust me and disobey my command. Did I not go against the wishes of my mother by marrying you? Why did you not trust my love? Since you prefer to believe your sisters rather than your lover, you had better go back to them. The only punishment for your disobedience is that I must leave you. Goodbye – love cannot live with suspicion.'

With these bitter words Eros once more spread his wings and flew back to his mother's temple to be healed of the burn on his shoulder. The wretched Psyche was left weeping and lamenting. For hours she cried, until at last she fell asleep from sorrow and exhaustion.

When Psyche awoke, the palace in its stately grove beside the crystal spring had disappeared. She found herself in a field near the city where her sisters lived. She went to them and told them of her misfortunes. They pretended to be sorry, but secretly they rejoiced. Now that the god had left Psyche for ever, might he not take one of them?

So next morning both the sisters rose early without telling anyone and went to the top of the mountain. First one, then the other called upon Zephyrus, spirit of the west wind, to carry her to his lord, the god Eros. Then she leaped into the air, but Zephyrus had not answered their call; so each was dashed to pieces as she fell down the steep slope of the mountain.

Psyche, meanwhile, wandered in every direction in search of her husband. She did not despair of finding him and winning back his love. One day she raised her eyes to the top of a hill on which stood a temple to Demeter, goddess of the harvests. Perhaps she might find her lover there. When she reached the temple, she found that it was filled with the fruits of the harvest – heaps of barley, millet, wheat and maize, all mixed up in a confused mass. Beside them were scattered the tools of the harvesters – rakes, sickles and implements for threshing the grain and binding the sheaves. It was as if the country people, overcome by the heat of the day, had flung everything into the temple, regardless of order. At once, to show her devotion to the gods, Psyche began to sort the grain and arrange the implements of the harvest in proper order. Demeter the goddess, seeing the girl at this pious work, took pity on her.

'Psyche,' said Demeter graciously, 'I am sorry for your distress. I cannot shield you from the anger of Aphrodite, but I can at least give you the best advice to help you in your unhappiness. Go and present yourself to her: ask for her forgiveness and beg her to tell you what you must do to regain her favour. This is the only way in which you may perhaps win back your lost husband.'

Psyche made her way towards the temple of Aphrodite, fearing the angry goddess, yet sure that Demeter was right: to try to please Aphrodite by humble submission and dutiful reverence was the only way by which she might hope for happiness.

Aphrodite was indeed very angry.

'At last,' she cried when Psyche appeared, her eyes lowered submissively to the ground, 'you realize that you have a mistress. At last you have come to show duty to the goddess to whom you show reverence. Or have you perhaps come to see your husband, who is still sick of the injury you did him when you dropped burning oil upon him? You have no hope but in showing how dutiful and humble you can be. How otherwise do you suppose a young man like my son can ever again bear to look on a creature so ugly and misshapen as you?'

To these insults Psyche made no answer but stood quietly before Aphrodite with her head bowed.

'I will make trial of you,' the goddess went on, 'to see how much patience and skill you are capable of.'

She led the girl to a storehouse at the back of her temple where there was a great heap of grain for her pigeons – wheat, lentils, barley and millet, such as birds love to feed and fatten on. But all the grain was sadly mixed up, just as in the temple of Demeter, only worse.

'You must sort out this grain by nightfall,' commanded the goddess. 'Put the wheat in one bin, the millet in another, and so on until not one grain is out of place. Do as I command.'

So saying, she left poor Psyche to her impossible task.

Psyche sat weeping before the enormous heap of grain and could do nothing. What was the use of beginning a task so hopeless? But Eros, who knew of her presence in the temple and of her plight, called up the leader of the ants and told her to help Psyche. The ant immediately set out from her home underground and made straight for the storehouse. She was followed by a train of other ants in their thousands, and before long they had carried all the grains to their proper bins and performed the task imposed by the cruel goddess.

Aphrodite, meanwhile, was enjoying a splendid banquet of the gods. When it was over, night had fallen. Crowned with roses and perfumed with celestial odours, she went to the storehouse. When she saw that the task had been performed to perfection, she was furious.

'Wicked girl!' she stormed. 'This is not your work. You have been helped by my son. You cannot get my favour by cheating.'

Without another word she flung Psyche a crust of dry bread for her supper and left her to herself.

Next morning the goddess sent for Psyche.

'Today,' she said, 'I have other work for you. Beside the river there is a grove of trees, and under them grazes a flock of sheep. There is no shepherd. The sheep have fleeces of fine golden wool. Fetch me a piece of the wool from every single sheep, and mind, do not miss out one of them. Be off with you!'

Psyche obediently went to the river bank, beyond which

stood the grove where grazed the sheep with the golden fleeces. As she was wondering how best to cross the water, a wind blew through the reeds, which seemed to speak to her with the voice of the river god.

'Dear Psyche,' the voice said, 'do not try to cross the river now and excite the anger of the fierce rams on the other side. They may tear you to pieces with their savage horns, for while the sun is rising towards noon, they are full of rage. But wait until the heat of noon has sent them into the shade. They are calmer then, and you will be able to cross the river in safety and make your way among them unharmed. You will find plenty of their wool sticking to the bushes and brambles in the grove.'

Psyche felt grateful to the kindly river god for his practical advice, which she began to follow as soon as the afternoon sun had driven the sheep and the fierce rams into the quiet shade. Going swiftly from bush to bush, she collected a huge armful of the golden fleeces and took them back to Aphrodite. The goddess received them with an ill grace.

'You could not have done this without the help from another,' she said sourly. 'I am still not persuaded that you ever manage to do anything useful by your own efforts. I have yet another task for you. Here, take this box and go with it down to the underworld. Present yourself at the temple of the queen, Persephone. Ask for her to put a little of her beauty in the box, that I might wear it tonight at the banquet of the gods. In looking after my sick son, wounded by your foolishness, I have lost a little of my own beauty and must repair it. Go at once, and do not be long.'

Left to herself with the box, Psyche now believed that her end had come. How could she, a mere unprotected mortal, go alone to the dreaded kingdom of Hades, the gloomy shades where all men fear to tread? So in order to bring upon herself the end which she felt to be near and get to the underworld by the quickest way, she climbed a hill on which stood a high tower. From this she prepared to throw herself to destruction. But the voice of an unseen presence called to her from the tower.

'Fair Psyche, why do you despair? Have you lost the courage that carried you through all previous trials? Is this the way to reach the underworld and fetch back what you have been told to fetch? No. There is a better way. I shall lead you to the entrance of a cave, through which you shall pass in safety to the kingdom of the dead. You shall pass unharmed the dreaded Cerberus, the three-headed monster who guards the entrance. Charon the ferryman shall row you in safety across the River Styx. Come, take my hand, and you shall have the courage to face the ordeal that lies before you.'

Then the unseen presence led Psyche to the entrance of the cave and bade her farewell.

'One thing I must warn you against,' said the voice. 'When you have got what you need, do not open the box and look into it. It is not for a mortal woman to pry into the secrets of divine beauty.'

Psyche did as she was told, obeying her adviser in every detail until she had returned safely from the dreaded journey.

She presented herself at the throne of Persephone and made known the wishes of Aphrodite. The queen of the underworld gave her what she requested, and Psyche returned by the way she had come, filled with joy and thanksgiving to see once more the light of the sun. She began to travel swiftly back towards her mistress Aphrodite, but curiosity seized her. She was suddenly overcome by an irrestible desire to see what was in the box. Perhaps a little of Persephone's beauty might alight on her own faded cheeks and make her more desirable than ever in the eyes of her husband, if ever she

should see him again. Swiftly she unclasped the lid of the box and opened it. In it she saw nothing. Nothing whatever was visible, and the box seemed full only of the intense darkness of death. From this arose the vapours of a profound sleep, which swirled about Psyche's head. Within a few instants she had fainted away and lay like one dead beside the road.

Eros meanwhile had recovered from his burn and was eager to see his beloved wife once more. He had forgiven her for her disobedience. He slipped through the open window of his room and flew by instinct to the place where Psyche lay. He knew at once what had happened. With his magic powers he gathered up the sleep from Psyche's body, replaced it in the box and closed the lid. Then he touched her with an arrow and she awoke.

'Oh, faithless Psyche,' said Eros, 'once more you have almost died through that same curiosity which made you break your promise to me. But you are safe. Go now to my mother and give her the box. Make haste, for she is waiting impatiently.'

As soon as Psyche had taken up the box and begun to make her way towards Aphrodite's temple, Eros rose swiftly into the air and presented himself at the throne of Zeus, chief of all the gods, on Mount Olympus. Zeus was awaiting the nightly banquet of the immortals, which was soon to begin. Eros pleaded with him for the life of his beloved and for the favour of Aphrodite, whom Psyche had offended unintentionally. Zeus was moved by the young man's entreaties. He sent his messenger Hermes of the winged feet to fetch Psyche up to the divine assembly. When Psyche appeared before him, Zeus greeted her and offered her a cup of nectar, the wine of the gods.

'Drink this, Psyche,' he said kindly, 'and be one of us – be immortal, even as a goddess.'

Then Zeus commanded that there should be a feast in honour of the marriage of Eros and Psyche, who were to remain united for ever. Thus, after many trials, the two lovers were joined in perpetual happiness in the company of the gods. Even proud Aphrodite forgave Psyche when she saw that her dear son could not be happy without her.

12

Ceyx and Alcyone

CEYX was King of Thessaly, where he ruled justly and peaceably. He was a handsome man and the son of Hesperus, the evening star. His dutiful and loving wife was Alcyone, daughter of Aeolus, in whose keeping are all the winds of heaven. Ceyx was in mourning for the death of his brother. At this event strange and terrible prodigies had occurred, and this made Ceyx afraid of what might come. He decided, therefore, to journey to Caros in Ionia, to consult the oracle of Apollo. When he told his wife Alcyone about this, she shuddered and turned pale.

'What is wrong?' asked Ceyx.

'Have I offended you, that you must leave me?' asked Alcyone. 'Do not make this voyage. It is dangerous to venture out to sea. Believe me, I know the winds, and they will do their worst to engulf you in storms and wreck your ship.'

Ceyx told her he must go.

'Well then,' said Alcyone, 'take me with you so that I may share your perils. Don't leave me at home to imagine your dangers and hardships.'

Ceyx would have liked to grant her wish, but he could not bear to expose her to the dangers of the sea. So he told her he must depart as soon as the wind permitted, and said farewell.

'I swear to you,' he said at parting, 'by my father Hesperus, the evening star, whom I call upon for his protection, that I will return to you before two full moons have shown themselves in the sky.'

With tears and vain entreaties Alcyone watched her husband as he stood on the deck of the ship, which slowly disappeared from view. Then she returned home, her heart full of foreboding, and threw herself on her bed in terror and despair. She feared she had seen the last of her beloved Ceyx.

Alcyone's fears were all too well founded. For when little more than half King Ceyx's course had been travelled, the winds rose, the waves swelled and whitened to angry foam and, as night came on, a storm burst over the ship. In vain did the sailors haul on their ropes and draw in the sails. In vain did they ship their oars and lash them to the sides of the vessel. Night fell swiftly, lit only by forked lightning and made terrible by the screeching of the wind and the crashing of thunder. Rain fell in torrents as if to make the whole world one mass of seething water.

Courage sank and hope failed. Death seemed certain. The sailors in despair thought of their homes and the loved ones they would see no more. Ceyx thought only of his wife Alcyone, whose name was ever on his lips, as if she were a goddess to whom he was praying. He longed for her comforting arms but rejoiced that she was safe at home in Thessaly.

Then the whole world seemed to explode in one tremendous crash. The mast broke in half and the rudder was torn from the ship's stern. Some of the sailors were swept off the decks, to sink in the boiling waves and rise no more. Others clutched at fragments of wreckage. Ceyx clung to a plank and shouted for help. His cries were in vain. With Alcyone's name upon his lips he was dashed from the plank by a wave as high as a palace. As he sank, he prayed that his body might be washed ashore at the feet of his wife. At least he would be mourned and buried by her he loved.

Alcyone, meanwhile, knew nothing of all this. She counted the days until her husband's return, busying herself in getting ready the palace and preparing the garments she would wear on the day of thanksgiving. She prayed incessantly to the gods for his safety, and especially to Hera, wife of Zeus, king of all the gods.

Gods alone are all-knowing, and Hera knew that Ceyx, for whom Alcyone prayed, was already dead. She could not bear to hear the vain prayers and entreaties of the Queen. Somehow she must be told of her husband's sad fate. So the goddess summoned her messenger, Iris, and sent her on an errand to the cave of the god of sleep. Iris, whom mortals see as the rainbow, put on her robe of many colours and sped across the sky. The cave of sleep was a dark and drowsy den, whence flowed Lethe, river of forgetfulness. On a black couch, draped in a cloak of sable, slept the god. Iris woke him up and said:

'I come from the goddess Hera. She commands you to send to Alcyone, Queen of Thessaly, a dream in which she will learn how Ceyx, her husband, was lately drowned in a storm at sea.'

The god called up Morpheus, one of his sons, and bade him go and present himself, in the form of the drowned Ceyx, at the bed of Alcyone as she slept. When he had done this, Iris sped away and the god of sleep yawned and closed his eyes.

Morpheus, who has the power to assume the shapes and voices of men, flew noiselessly to the palace of Alcyone. There he laid aside his dusky wings and took on the shape of a drowned man, his hair and beard coated with salt, his limbs entwined with seaweed. Then he stood in the pale half-light of early dawn at the foot of Alcyone's bed.

'Do you recognize your husband Ceyx?' he asked, tears streaming from his salt-reddened eyes. He spoke with the voice of the drowned king. 'I am the spirit of your husband, lost in the stormy sea. Pray no more for my return, but give me your tears and lamentations, so that I may go to the underworld mourned by her I never ceased to love and to call upon even as the waves filled my mouth.'

Alcyone, on hearing these words, groaned in her sleep and stretched forth her hands to embrace her husband's ghost. But Morpheus vanished and, as Alcyone awoke, she knew that her dream had been a vision of the truth.

'My fears did not deceive me,' she cried in her agony. 'Now I know the cruel waves have devoured him. He should have taken me with him, so that in death we would not have been divided. I cannot live without him. I must go and share his death.'

It was now dawn. Quickly the Queen arose and prepared for her last journey. She hastened down to the seashore and found the spot near the harbour where she had last seen her husband. There, not two months ago, she had gazed out to sea and watched the sails of his ship disappearing over the horizon, bearing the man she loved to his destruction. Then, as she looked out across the water, she saw something floating gently towards the land. The waves, now peaceful, carried it steadily nearer. At last Alcyone could see that it was the body of a drowned man. She trembled and clasped her hands together in torment as she recognized the body as that of Ceyx. She stretched out her arms towards it and cried:

'Is this your promised return, my loved one? Is it thus that you come back to me over the pitiless ocean?'

A mole or breakwater had been built out into the sea to protect the harbour from the force of the waves. From this Alcyone could get nearer to the floating form of Ceyx. With-

144

out a moment's hesitation she ran to the end of the mole and leaped into the water to join her husband, from whom she could not bear to be parted. But at the instant of her leap she was changed into a bird and flew skimming across the water. From her throat, in the voice of a bird, came a song of deepest lamentation. She alighted on the waves beside the pale body of her husband, enfolding it in her wings. With her horny beak she strove to kiss the lifeless body. At this Ceyx too was changed into a living bird. The faithful pair were thus reunited as a reward by the gods for their devotion to each other. They mated and had their brood of young ones every year.

So was born the race of the kingfisher, known to the Greeks by the name of Alcyone or, as we call it, the Halcyon. Each winter, for seven calm days, Alcyone broods over her nest, which floats peacefully upon the waves. By this mariners may know that the sea is safe to voyage over, and Aeolus, father of Alcyone, controls the winds and will not let them arise to drive the storm clouds across the sea. In these few halcyon days the sea is the playground of Aeolus's grandchildren, the little kingfishers.

13

Orpheus and Eurydice

APOLLO, god of the Sun and greatest of all musicians, had a son by the Muse Calliope. The Muses were nine goddesses who lived on Mount Helicon and inspired poets, writers and musicians. The son of Apollo and Calliope was called Orpheus.

As might be expected of the son of such gifted parents, Orpheus proved to have more than ordinary talent for music. His father gave him a lyre of great beauty, cunningly fashioned so that the music of its seven strings was of unusual power and sweetness. But greater than the sweetness of the lyre was the skill of its owner. As the young man, dark-haired and with shining eyes, went about the countryside singing to the strains of his lyre, not only did men and women marvel to hear him; even mountains seemed to be raising their heads in wonder. The streams stayed their rushing to listen to him, and even the very rocks lost some of their hardness at the sound of his music. He became familiar among the woods and mountains of Thrace, which were inhabited by wild animals. But Orpheus went in no fear of even the fiercest creature; for such was the power of his music that the very wolves and lions would lie down at his feet and draw in their claws, lulled to gentleness as the young man's fingers moved over the strings of his lyre. The harmless creatures, the fawn and the antelope, would stretch themselves out beside the lion, sensing that even the king of beasts would not harm them so long as Orpheus played and sang. The trees crowded together about the musician, giving shade to him and his audience; the winds were still, and in the branches sat the dove and the eagle, side by side. Never before had such music charmed the ear of man and beast alike.

In Thrace lived the nymphs of stream and woodland, and they too came to listen to Orpheus. The wood nymphs were called Dryads, and among them the most beautiful was Eurydice. No sooner did she cast eyes on the young musician than she fell in love with him. Raising his head from the lyre, Orpheus as quickly fell in love with the Dryad, and resolved to marry her. Their courting was not long, and soon they had agreed to become man and wife. But at the wedding ceremony Fate was not on their side. For when Hymen, the god of marriage, held aloft the lighted torch, it burned, not with a clear golden flame, but with black smoke which drifted over the assembly in a thick and ominous cloud. So the eyes of the crowd, instead of being filled with joy, smarted with tears of pain. In vain did Orpheus play his best; in vain the nymphs prayed to the gods to send better omens.

Not long afterwards Eurydice and the other Dryads were wandering through the woods when a young man named Aristaeus caught sight of her and determined to win her for himself. He tried to seize her, but she fled from him through the trees, and he pursued her. In her flight Eurydice chanced to step on a snake in the grass. It bit her foot, and she died of the poison. Aristaeus, her pursuer, was a shepherd and a bee-keeper, and after the death of Eurydice the nymphs, her companions, poisoned his bees in revenge, so that they died.

So great was the shock to Orpheus that he could not believe

Eurydice was really dead. Might not his music, that had moved even stones, soften the hearts of the gods? For they were all-powerful and could give him back his wife if they wished. So Orpheus played upon his lyre more ravishingly than ever, raising his voice in sorrowful lamentation. The gods of the earth were moved, but they could do nothing for him, since the dead do not stay upon the earth but descend into the realm of the stern god Hades and his queen, Persephone. Here in the timeless shades the spirits of the dead wander aimlessly, and never look again upon the green fields and woods of the upper world.

In despair Orpheus went to seek his lost wife in the regions of the dead. He went down into the underworld by a steep and narrow way which began in a gloomy cave. Down and down the path wound until it reached the grey and dreary realm of Hades. Passing through crowds of ghosts, Orpheus made his way towards the throne of the king and queen. At the sight of the wild-eyed musician with his lyre, the god Hades raised his hand for silence and bade the stranger play. With his right hand Orpheus struck the lyre and, lifting his voice, began to plead and mourn in tones which moved the hardest hearts and brought tears to the eyes of many.

'O god and goddess,' sang Orpheus, 'to whom we must all come at last, listen, I pray, to my tale, for I speak the truth. Perhaps you ask why I, a living man, have come of my own free will to your kingdom. I am not here to spy out the secrets of Hades nor to fight against the monster who guards your gates. I am come to plead for your mercy and to beg you to give back life to my beloved Eurydice, who was slain by the cruel viper when our wedding rites were scarcely over. Give her back to me, I beg, for she has done no harm and broken no vow. Gods of the underworld, we shall all come under your rule in time. When our time has come, we shall give thanks to the gods for our love and our lives, but until she has lived her proper span, give her back to me, I implore you.'

So piteously did Orpheus lament, with such skill did he draw harmony from the strings that the inhabitants of Hades came from near and far to hear his music. The ghosts came in crowds, like flocks of birds coming home to roost at dusk, or like showers of dead leaves driven by the autumn wind. There were boys and men, unmarried girls, the spirits of great heroes and of nameless ones who had died in battle on land or sea. All who heard were touched to the heart by the music of Orpheus; all pitied the young man whose loss had inspired him to songs never heard before on earth or in the underworld.

Among those who heard Orpheus were the prisoners in Hades, doomed to suffer eternal punishment for their crimes on earth. Tantalus was one. He was condemned to lie beneath a tree at the edge of a pool. Every time he stretched out his hand to gather fruit, a wind blew the branches out of reach. Every time he approached the pool to quench his thirst, the water drew back. Another was Ixion, whose punishment was to be tied to a wheel which turned for ever. When Orpheus sang, the wheel stood still, and Ixion was for a while relieved of his torment. Sisyphus, for his crimes on earth, was condemned to roll a heavy stone up a hill; as soon as it reached the top, it rolled down again, so that his labour was eternal. For the first time he was allowed to rest upon his stone half-way up the hill, while Orpheus lamented. For the first time, too, the cheeks of the Furies were wet with tears. These were among the most terrible deities in Hades – three winged women whose purpose was to avenge crimes against family ties, such as the killing of a parent or child. Some say that their look was made fiercer by writhing serpents which crowned their heads, like the serpents of the gorgon Medusa.

Now even the snakes ceased their writhing and hissing to listen to Orpheus.

By the time the song was finished, Persephone, queen of the underworld, could not restrain her pity, and with tear-filled eyes she looked at her husband and pleaded for the life of Eurydice. Hades, stern king, consented, and the young bride was summoned from among the newly arrived ghosts. Limping upon her wounded foot, Eurydice appeared, pale and beautiful, before the throne. Long and lovingly Orpheus looked at her, but he dared not approach until the king had given his judgement. Because of his steadfastness in love, said the king, Orpheus would be allowed to take her back to the earth on one condition: he was to lead the way, and Eurydice would follow. He must not look back at her, even for an instant, until they reached the upper air. If he did, he would lose her once more – this time for ever.

Eagerly Orpheus embraced his wife. Then, taking leave of the king and queen, they began the journey back to earth. Orpheus went in front, Eurydice behind, as they had been bidden. Once the gloomy regions of ghosts were passed, they came to a place of terrible darkness and silence, groping their way between rocks and through dark passages where icy water dripped about them, and jagged rocks tore their clothes. Then they began to climb, up and up along the winding track by which Orpheus had come. Panting, he reached a sort of ledge or platform not far from where the track led into the cave where it would end in the light of day. Suddenly a madness overcame Orpheus. A terrible fear for his loved Eurydice made him forget his promise to the king of the underworld. He looked back to see if he could make out her form in the darkness behind him, and in that instant she was lost to him.

A great roll of thunder came from the underworld beneath,

as if the Furies were expressing their wrath at Orpheus's forgetfulness. There is no forgiveness in Hades. Amidst the thunder Orpheus heard the voice of Eurydice:

'O Orpheus, the Fates are calling me back. Unseen hands are dragging me down. I feel faint, and I no longer have any power to resist.'

In vain did Orpheus stretch out his arms to embrace her. She floated like a cloud of grey smoke back into the depths of Hades. He had lost her for ever.

For seven months Orpheus wandered amidst the desolate rocks and mountains of Thrace, lamenting the second death of Eurydice in strains which softened the stones about him and melted the hard hearts of wolves and lions. But his song had no power to pierce the ears of the guardians of the underworld, and he called down bitter curses upon their heads.

'O gloomy powers,' he sang, 'O savage Furies, let an everlasting curse fall upon your flinty hearts. Wolves are not too cruel to be moved; granite cliffs are softened by my grief. You alone remain immovable in your unjust and hellish fury against one whose only fault was to love too much the wife you have taken from him.'

The story of Orpheus's death is as sad as that of Eurydice's, and more terrible. The Thracian nymphs, Eurydice's former companions, tried to console Orpheus, but he would not listen to them. He wished only to be left to mourn for his wife alone. But they pursued him with sweet songs and wooed him with garlands of flowers.

'Eurydice is dead,' they said. 'She will never return again. Take another wife. Take one of us, and she will make you happier than ever you were before.'

Still Orpheus would not listen, and in the end the nymphs'

love was turned to hate. They now wished only to destroy Orpheus.

One day they were celebrating the festival of the god Dionysus. The music and dancing maddened them, and one of them, seeing Orpheus a long way off, cried:

'See, there is the man who scorns us, the man who despises our kindness and love. He no longer deserves to live!'

Swiftly she ran, spear in hand, to where Orpheus was playing a sad lament on his lyre. When she was within range, she hurled the spear. But the spear was turned away from Orpheus by the power of his music. So also were the stones which other maidens threw at the young man. At this the enraged nymphs lifted their voices in a scream of anger, which utterly drowned the notes of the lyre. Orpheus's music had no longer any power to protect him, and in a moment a spear struck him in the breast and he was killed. Then the shrieking nymphs tore his body limb from limb and flung the remains far and wide. They cut off his head, and threw it, together with the lyre, into the River Hebrus. Such was the revenge of Eurydice's former companions on her unhappy husband. Such was his reward for loving her too dearly.

The head of Orpheus floated slowly down the river, the lyre beside it. His eyes were closed and his black hair, stained with blood, streamed behind him. From his open mouth came a long last lament; and magical notes sounded from the floating lyre, so that the trees along the river bank bowed their heads in sympathy, and the shores echoed with the dead man's sorrow. At last the head of Orpheus reached the island of Lesbos, where it was buried. The lyre was taken up by the gods and given a place among the stars in heaven. Orpheus's mother, Calliope, and her sister Muses gathered up the torn limbs and buried them in a grove in Libethra. Here, it is said, the nightingales sing over the grave of Orpheus with a more piercing sweetness than in any other part of Greece.

The spirit of Orpheus went down to the underworld, where once the living man had been. Eagerly he sought the spirit of his dead Eurydice and together they wander through the grey wastes of Hades, happy in each other's company, happy in the knowledge that never again can they be divided.

14

Theseus

1 The Journey to Athens

QUEEN AETHRA lived in Troizen with her little son Theseus. His father Aegeus had left Troizen to become king of Athens. Before he left, he had raised a great stone and laid under it a pair of enchanted sandals and curved sword in a sheath of ivory. He told Aethra that as soon as their son was strong enough to raise the stone, he was to take the sword and the sandals and make his way to Athens, where he would reign as king after his father.

Golden-haired Theseus grew straight and strong, learning to run and wrestle like the other boys of Troizen. Soon he became their leader, for he was a more powerful wrestler than they, and a faster runner. He could leap further and higher than all the others, and throw the javelin straighter. He was, too, a fine hunter, taking great delight in pursuing the leopard and the antelope through the vales and hills that lay about his home. Everyone acknowledged the strength, the courage and the manly grace of the young prince.

More than once the boy looked at the great stone which, as his mother had told him, hid the gifts left by his father. As little boys, he and his companions had often made pretence of raising it to see what was underneath, but many years were to pass before even Theseus, the strongest of them, was able to lift it so much as an inch from the ground. How Theseus longed to claim possession of his birthright and go in search of adventure, as the hero Heracles had done before him.

At last the day came, as Aethra knew it must. One fine spring morning the young man, for such he now was, bestrode the great stone, bent over it, placed the fingers of both hands beneath the farther edge and heaved with all his might. Almost before he knew he had succeeded, he felt the stone yield to his strength. Leaping aside, he was in time to avoid it as it toppled over backwards, revealing a cavity underneath. In it were the bright sword in its ivory scabbard and the enchanted sandals, just as his father had left them all those years before.

'Now,' said Theseus to his mother, 'I have won my birthright, and I must set out at once to greet my father in Athens, just as you have always said I should.'

Half in tears and half in joy, Aethra gave orders that a sacrifice should be made at the temple, in order that her son should have protection when he set out on the morrow. The wise men of Troizen counselled the youth to set sail and cross the gulf which divided their land from Athens. But Theseus had other plans. The country between was infested with brigands and monsters, who harassed and terrorized the people. Simply to take the short way by sea would be to avoid all these dangers and lose the chance to prove himself a hero. So Theseus determined to go the long way round by land. Heracles, his hero, would have done the same. The youth could then prove his strength and courage, and show himself fit to reign in Athens when the time came. In vain did the elders plead with him to take the easier way.

So next morning, as the sun rose over the eastern hills, the golden-haired youth made his sacrifice to the gods, embraced his mother, and bade farewell to the companions of his boyhood. All cheered and wished him luck as he strode out to seek his fame and fortune. The sword was buckled securely by his side and the enchanted sandals bore him swiftly on his way. It was not long before he met his first adventure.

At Epidaurus, not far along the road, the ground was strewn with human bones, the grisly remains of the victims of the giant Periphetes, known to all the countryside as the Club-bearer. With a roar the giant plunged from a thicket and bore straight down upon the young man, brandishing above his shoulders the great bronze club which was the terror of all who came that way. The giant commanded Theseus to go no further, but Theseus, stepping nimbly aside as the monstrous weapon came crashing down, turned swiftly and struck Periphetes with his sword. For a while the two fought desperately, filling the air with their heavy breathing and with cries of pain or triumph. At length the youth and nimbleness of the young man began to tell. Periphetes's breath came more heavily, and the terrible blows of his club fell more slowly about the young man's body. He began to fear that at last he had met his match. Already wounded more than once, he suddenly fell to the ground as Theseus aimed a deadly stroke at his heart. The fight was over. The giant lay dead on the ground, and the bronze club rolled from his grasp. Triumphantly Theseus replaced his sword in the sheath at his side and picked up the club. This, he was determined, was his weapon by right, and for the rest of his journey he carried it with him. Heavy as it was, he could wield it with scarcely an effort.

The shepherds and shepherdesses of the region came to pay homage to the young hero and thank him for their deliverance from the dreaded Club-bearer. Then, as they cheered him on his way, they warned him of the next danger he would meet further along the road to Athens. This was a cruel man named

Sinis, known as the Pine-bender. The reason for his nickname was this: it was his delight to seize an unlucky traveller and bind him fast with ropes. Then, such was his mighty strength, he would bend two young pines to the ground until they almost touched each other, and tie his victim partly to one tree, partly to the other. Then he would let them go, and the miserable traveller would be torn in half and his limbs flung far and wide, to be devoured by vultures. Part might hang from the tops of the trees, a ghastly warning to others.

Theseus strode towards the haunt of the Pine-bender. It was not long before he encountered him. The man rudely ordered the young wayfarer to stop and give himself up. For answer Theseus ran towards him, flourishing the bronze club he had taken from Periphetes.

'This weapon I took from the giant Periphetes!' he cried. 'As I served him, so shall I serve all tyrants!'

So great was the surprise of Sinis at Theseus's defiance that he had no time to step aside as the bronze club was swung through the air. Felled to the ground, he screamed for mercy, but Theseus swiftly bound him with ropes and tied him to two of the trees in the grove where he had for so long spread terror. When Theseus let go of the saplings, the Pine-bender himself was torn asunder and his remains fed the crows for miles around. So ended yet another monster in human shape, and the neighbourhood was made safe for travellers.

The next episode in Theseus's progress to Athens took place near the town of Crommyon. Here he heard reports of yet another enemy to peaceful people – not a tyrant or a giant this time but a monstrous wild sow. This ferocious animal lurked in the woods about the town, preying on sheep and young pigs, frightening the farmers and even attacking young children, who ran screaming to their parents if they so much as caught sight of the beast. At once Theseus strode off into the woods where it had last been reported. He had not gone far before he heard the crackling of dry leaves and undergrowth. Then in a clearing he caught sight of the sow. It was of enormous size and covered all over with spiky bristles. Its short, powerful legs dug into the ground as it rushed towards the young man, snorting with savage fury. One blow of the great club was sufficient to knock the monster senseless. Then he cut off its head and bore it in triumph back to Crommyon, where his victory was celebrated with feasts and dancing. The countryside was rid for ever of one more danger.

As Theseus went on, his feet made lighter by the enchanted sandals, the road became steeper and rougher. Presently it was no more than a narrow track between the hills and the sea. A passing stranger warned him of the presence of the bandit Sciron, who haunted the craggy cliff that bore his name. It was the bandit's practice, the stranger told Theseus, to make everyone who came that way kneel down and wash his feet. Then he would seize the man while he knelt and pitch him headlong over the cliff into the sea far below. Here lurked a great tortoise, who waited to devour Sciron's victims. Thus, said the stranger, cautious wayfarers like himself were obliged to go inland and take a longer way round in order to avoid the bandit.

Theseus thanked the stranger for his warning – but nothing would turn him from his course. Up the steep path he went until he came to the summit of Sciron's cliff. Everything turned out just as he had been told. Astride the narrow path stood Sciron, an uncouth and brawny ruffian, his face scarcely visible through the shaggy locks that hung down about it.

'Young man!' roared Sciron as soon as Theseus came into view. 'You shall not pass this way before doing as I order you. I demand of all comers that they kneel down at my feet and wash them, for I am lord of this land.'

Instantly the young man obeyed, going down on one knee before the bandit. Taking a filthy rag that Sciron gave him, he prepared to wash his feet.

'Place your right foot on my knee, Master,' he said cunningly, 'so that I may do your bidding.'

As soon as Sciron's foot was firmly on his knee, Theseus sprang up, seized the bandit by the wrist and twisted him over his shoulder before he knew what was happening. It was a trick that he had learnt when wrestling as a boy in Troizen. With a roar of surprise and anger, Sciron attempted to escape from Theseus's grasp. But the young man was too quick for him. The bandit was hurled over the edge of the cliff, his arms and legs whirling in all directions. Nothing could save him, though what became of him is not quite certain. Some say he was devoured by the very tortoise to which he had fed so many hapless victims. Others say that he escaped the tortoise but was turned into a rock which can be seen to this very day under the cliff that bears his name.

Another evil-doer whom Theseus encountered as he drew nearer to Athens was a man named Procrustes or the Stretcher. He had a particularly cruel way of dealing with his victims. If he saw a harmless traveller who looked as if he was tired, he would invite him with a show of courtesy to accept the hospitality of his cottage. In it he had a bedstead on which he invited his guest to lie down. But he insisted that the traveller should fit the bed exactly. If he was too short, Procrustes stretched his limbs until they were long enough. Thus the bedstead was really an instrument of torture. If the unfortunate guest was too long, however Procrustes lopped off enough of his legs to make him fit. When Theseus reached the cottage of this horrible butcher, he was invited inside, as other travellers were.

'You look tired,' said Procrustes. 'Won't you lie down on

the bed I keep for my guests?'

Theseus made as if to do so; then, as Procrustes prepared to tie him down, he jumped up and seized his attacker by the throat. A wrestling match followed. Both men fought with furious determination, but the young man was more than a match for Procrustes. When the torturer was tied safely to his own bedstead and could struggle no more, Theseus said:

'As my enemies use other men, so they are used by me!'

Although Procrustes exactly fitted the bedstead, Theseus ended his life by cutting off his head. In this way he freed the country for ever from one more evil brigand.

Thus the young hero overcame all the dangers of the journey, but his greatest danger lay ahead. It awaited him in Athens itself, where his father Aegeus reigned with the sorceress Medea, who had been the wife of Jason, as his queen. It must be remembered that Aegeus had never seen Theseus since he was a baby, so that he had no idea that the unknown young hero who strode into Athens in triumph was his own son. But Medea knew by means of witchcraft, and she wanted the throne of Athens for her own son. She feared that Theseus, being the king's eldest child, would take the throne and the kingdom for himself. This she determined to prevent at all costs. She murmured in the king's ear that the young stranger was coming to plot against him and raise a rebellion.

'I know this, by magic arts,' she told Aegeus. 'Your only hope is to rid the kingdom of him before he wins the hearts of the people and makes himself popular. He is even now on his way to the palace. I have prepared a draught of wine and have put into it a few drops of poison which I myself have distilled from herbs. He will die instantly.'

Aegeus was a weak man and agreed to allow his queen to kill the young man in this way.

Amidst the applause of some citizens of Athens who had

already heard of Theseus's brave exploits, the hero walked swiftly and gracefully down the great hall to where Aegeus sat on his royal throne. The king rose and greeted him. Then he held out the cup of wine which Medea had prepared. Theseus was about to raise it to his lips when suddenly his father noticed the carved ivory scabbard of the sword which he himself had left long ago under the stone in far-off Troizen.

'My son, my son!' he cried. 'Do not drink! The wine is poisoned.'

As he spoke, he dashed the cup from Theseus's hand, and the wine spilled harmlessly on the floor. There was a moment of astonished silence. Then Aegeus ordered the palace guards to seize Medea. But she had already fled from the hall. The instant she saw that Aegeus recognized Theseus, she knew that her plot had failed. Before anyone knew what had become of her, she had leapt into her winged chariot and was borne high in the air by enchantment. She did not stop till she had travelled far east into Asia and was never more seen in Greece.

Meanwhile Theseus had recovered from his amazement. He eagerly admitted that he was the son of Aethra and had taken the sword from under the stone, as had been ordained. Aegeus embraced his son and ordered a great feast to celebrate the coming of the young hero. Golden-haired Theseus glowed with triumph as he told the story of his adventures on the road to Athens. Garlanded by a cheering throng, he displayed the sword and its carved ivory sheath and the terrible bronze weapon he had won from the dreaded Club-bearer when first he began his journey. So Theseus remained many days in Athens, sharing his glory with the father he had so long desired to see.

2 The Minotaur

FOR a long time Theseus continued to live in Athens at his father's palace. He was honoured by all the people for his brave deeds, and he continued to fight against the enemies of Athens, winning for himself new renown every day. Then came the spring, and with it sadness fell upon the city.

The reason for it was this. Far to the south in an island named Crete lived King Minos, the ruler of the sea. He had had a son who had journeyed to Athens some years before to take part in the games. He was a splendid wrestler and runner, and King Aegeus had become jealous of his success. So he had the son of Minos murdered. This was a shameful deed, and Minos was quick to take revenge. He sent warships to make battle against the Athenians, and such damage did he do that Aegeus was forced to beg for peace. Minos made peace on one condition – and very harsh and grievous it was. Each spring seven young men and seven girls were to be sent to Crete as food for the monster called the Minotaur. This creature had the head and horns of a bull and the body of a man. It was kept in a maze or labyrinth which had been cunningly constructed by the great craftsman Daedalus so that, once inside it, it was almost impossible to find the way out. The Minotaur's food was human flesh, and Minos was obliged to feed it on living people.

So every spring the Athenians were forced to choose seven youths and seven girls by lot, and they were sent in a ship with black sails as tribute to King Minos. Great was the sorrow that fell upon the people of Athens: and spring, which should have been a season of rejoicing, was a season of mourning. Instead of feasts and dancing they went about weeping and sorrowing, as one by one their children or their brothers and sisters were chosen to be food of the monster.

As soon as he knew of this yearly sacrifice, Theseus determined to put an end to it. When lots were being drawn as to which of the wretched youths of Athens were to be sacrificed, he spoke to his father.

'Father,' he said, 'I will myself go with the ship to Crete. Either I shall slay this terrible creature, this bull-headed man, or I shall be killed.'

'No, my son,' cried Aegeus. 'You must not go. The lot has not fallen on you, and I cannot allow it. You are to be king of Athens when I die. That is your fate, not death in the labyrinth in Crete.'

'If other young men of Athens go,' argued Theseus, 'why should not I? Let me take the same chance with the others. Am I not the slayer of the giant Periphetes, the pine-bender Sinis, and the villain Procrustes? I am not frightened of the Minotaur. I shall go with the others.'

Aegeus was obliged to give in. With a heavy heart he saw his son join the six other young men and the seven girls, and go aboard the ship with the black sails. It was arranged that, when the ship returned to Athens, the sails should be changed for white ones if the voyage had been successful. If not – if Theseus was slain by the Cretan monster – the sails were to remain black.

All the citizens of Athens were gathered by the quay, as slowly the sails were hoisted and the ship began to move away to the south. Bitter tears were shed by the mothers and fathers, the brothers and sisters, of those in the ship. But with a high heart golden-haired Theseus stood at the stern of the ship and waved farewell to his grieving yet proud father. Sacrifices were offered to the gods and prayers were said in the temples, begging for the safe return of the expedition.

All too quickly the voyage was over. The servants and

soldiers of King Minos were awaiting the arrival of the Athenians in Crete to escort the unwilling party to the palace of the King. The palace and grounds were of the utmost magnificence and splendour, but the luckless youths and maidens had no eyes for its beauty. Nevertheless, Minos received them courteously and asked them to partake of a banquet in their honour. They were to stay overnight at his palace, and in the morning they would be driven through the great bronze gate of the labyrinth as food for the monstrous Minotaur.

At the banquet, Ariadne, the daughter of the king, could not take her eyes off the handsome stranger who was the leader of the party. She fell in love with Theseus at first sight and determined to save him if she could. After the banquet she walked with him in the palace grounds, and as they walked she said:

'Handsome Athenian, I am grieved that you and your companions must be sacrificed tomorrow. It is a terrible thing.'

'Then ask your father to spare us,' said Theseus.

'He will not listen to me. He is stern and revengeful. Every year it has been my unhappy lot to see your young men and maidens go away to be slain by the Minotaur. My father will only say that the monster, which is sacred, must have human victims.'

'Then how can you help us?'

'If I can find a way of helping you, you must take me back to Athens with you, for there will be no safety for me in Crete if it is found out that I have helped you.'

'Very well. You shall come with us. But how are we to bring this about?'

Cautiously Ariadne drew a sword from under her cloak and gave it to Theseus.

'It is enchanted,' she told him. 'No creature can withstand this sword.'

Then she handed to him a ball of woollen thread.

'Take this too,' she said. 'You will need it.'

'What for?' said Theseus.

'Once you have slain the Minotaur, you must find your way out of the maze. When you get in, tie one end of the wool to the doorpost and let the ball unroll as you go. You have only to follow the wool back and you will find your way out.'

Theseus listened carefully to these instructions, and early in the morning the young men and maidens were led to the entrance of the maze. Their guards opened the great bronze door and drove them in. As soon as the door was locked behind them, Theseus bade his companions remain hidden close to the beginning of the maze. They wished him good fortune as he fastened the end of the woollen ball to the doorpost and made his way forward, gripping firmly in his right hand the sword which Ariadne had given him. Through the cunning labyrinth he stole, this way and that, listening intently for any sound the hidden monster might make. As he went, the ball of wool gradually unwound, until very little of it was left in the pocket of his tunic. Suddenly he heard the sound of snorting and the scuffling of some clumsy body. He judged that the Minotaur must be round the next corner of the passage he was exploring. Almost before he knew it, the creature was in front of him, scarcely a stone's throw away. He saw the great black head, the cruel horns, the wicked eyes, and even Theseus's heart began to thump. Nevertheless, he tightened his grip on the sword and awaited the charge that must surely come. Sure enough, the Minotaur lowered its head, gave a terrifying bellow and rushed towards Theseus. Nimbly the young man jumped to one side, and as the monster passed him, he aimed a sword thrust at its neck. The monster howled with pain and rage, then turned at the end of its charge, and charged again. So the fight went on, until at length the Minotaur had received so many sword wounds that its strength began to fail. At last, with a blood-chilling groan it gave up the struggle and rolled on the ground, dead.

Hardly stopping to make sure that his victim breathed no more, Theseus searched for the end of the woollen thread, found it, and hurried back along the track by which he had come, twisting and turning until he found himself at the entrance of the labyrinth.

Great was the joy of his companions when they saw their leader return in triumph. They knew as soon as they saw the blood on his arms and tunic that he had been successful. While Theseus had been battling with the Minotaur, Ariadne, having obtained the key by telling the guards a falsehood, had unlocked the door and greeted the young Athenians as they left the hated place. Then she hid them in a temple until the coming of dusk made it safe for them all to slip down to the harbour. Theseus thanked Ariadne for her help, and together they got aboard the ship in safety and hoisted sail.

The voyage began joyfully, for a favourable wind carried the ship swiftly over the blue waves away from the hated shores of Crete. The monster that had devoured so many of the youth of Athens was slain, and never again would the tribute have to be paid.

Then the wind changed, and the ship was carried towards the island of Naxos, where Theseus decided to put in for the night. The ship was made fast, and the Athenians, together with the Cretan princess, made their way ashore. Here they feasted, and then lay down to rest. But during the night some god or goddess sent forgetfulness into the mind of Theseus, so that all thought of Ariadne was driven out of it. In his haste to return to Athens he forgot the princess who had helped him to save his companions, and whom he had promised to take home with him. Terrible was the grief of Ariadne when she rose soon after dawn and saw the ship far out to sea. She felt cruelly deserted, and for days went disconsolately up and down the shore weeping and calling upon the gods to save her from whatever destruction awaited her in that savage and inhospitable place.

Perhaps it was the god Dionysus who had made Theseus forgetful of his promise to Ariadne. For Dionysus had seen her from afar and fallen in love with her beauty. He determined to make her his bride. He was the god of feasting and merriment, of wine and laughter. In the depths of her despair Ariadne was therefore amazed and delighted to hear the sounds of mirth and song as Dionysus and his companions came in a wild procession from the woods. The god was throned high in a chariot drawn by leopards, and behind him followed the goat-footed satyrs who were his train. Their

169

brows were wreathed with vines and myrtle, the signs of merry-making, and over their shoulders hung great leathern bottles of wine. When the procession drew near to Ariadne, Dionysus leapt from his chariot and greeted her. They fell in love at first sight: the god lifted the princess into his chariot and carried her off to become his bride. So Ariadne soon forgot her grief at being deserted by Theseus.

Meanwhile in Athens, Aegeus and all the people anxiously awaited the return of the ship. So eager was the old king to know the fate of his beloved son that he stood on the cliffs hour after hour, gazing towards the horizon. At last the ship came into view, but the triumph of Theseus's homecoming was dimmed by tragedy. For a second time the young hero forgot a promise. He had undertaken, if his mission were successful, to change the black sails for white, and this he had forgotten to do. On seeing the black sails looming nearer and nearer, Aegeus was overcome by unbearable grief. He knew – or thought he knew – that his son had been killed by the Cretan monster. With a great groan of anguish and despair, Aegeus rushed to the edge of the cliff and threw himself headlong into the waves. From that day to this the name of the sea in which the king drowned himself has been the Aegean.

Thus the end of Theseus's voyage was one of mingled sorrow and rejoicing – sorrow at his father's fate, and joy at the triumph of the hero who had saved the whole city from its terrible ordeal. After a due time of mourning, Theseus was crowned King of Athens, and so came into the birthright he had been promised in his earliest days in far Troizen.

15

Arion

ARION, a poet and musician, was the son of Oncaea and the sea-god Poseidon. His fame as a composer and performer on the lyre spread throughout Greece. He was celebrated as the inventor of a wild kind of song known as a dithyramb. People were drawn towards his music from far and near. Like Orpheus, he had the power to attract even animals with the strains of his music.

He became a favourite of King Periander of Corinth and spent much of his time at the court. Arrayed in his singing-robe of resplendent purple and gold, he would sweep the strings of his lyre and raise his voice in strange and tragic music which would silence even the most talkative of Periander's courtiers.

One day Arion said to his master:

'I hear there is to be a contest for musicians in the island of Sicily across the sea. I would dearly like to go and take part.'

'Stay here with me,' urged Periander. 'Sicily is a long way off. Those who strive for fame far from their native shores often come to disaster.'

'I am a poet,' said Arion, 'and the heart of a poet loves a wandering life. If I win the contest, I will come back covered with glory and will add new lustre to your court here in Corinth.'

'Besides,' Periander went on, 'I shall miss you. We shall all miss you and your music.'

'It will not be for long,' replied Arion. 'I will return as soon as the festival is over.'

So he went. It would take too long to say how he fared in Sicily. It is enough to know that he won the contest and received a handsome reward in gold and silver. So great was his prize that he was able to buy presents for Periander and all his friends in Corinth and have a great sum left for himself. With these he embarked on a ship bound for home. It was a ship belonging to Periander.

The sea was calm, the wind light, the sky a cloudless blue. Arion's heart rose high.

'Periander,' he cried, 'I shall soon be back home. You had no cause to fear. The voyage will have been a triumph, and my fortunes are made. What a splendid reunion we will have as we sacrifice to the gods and especially to my father Poseidon and gather round the festive table to celebrate my triumph.'

But there was something he had forgotten – the treachery of greedy men. One day, while the ship still sailed smoothly on towards Greece, he chanced to overhear some of the sailors muttering among themselves. They knew of the great treasure he had aboard and were plotting to throw him into the sea and keep it for themselves. Before he had time to take in their words, they had gathered round him and were threatening his life.

'You must die, Arion,' said the leader of the sailors. 'If you wish to be buried on land, we will kill you here and take your body ashore with us. If you prefer a watery grave, throw yourself in the sea and swim for it.'

'Spare my life,' pleaded Arion, seeing that resistance was hopeless. 'Of what use is it to you? Take my treasure. I will give it to you freely in exchange for my life.'

They refused his request. They told him he must die. How could they live in safety to enjoy the treasure if Arion was alive to tell the tale?

In vain Arion pleaded with them, but they would not listen.

'Very well, then,' he said gravely. 'Since I am to die, let me die as I have lived. Let me die the death of a poet and a singer. I will sing a last song to commend my soul to the gods. As soon as I have played and sung, I will yield myself up to you without complaint.'

They agreed, for a few of them indeed had sufficient curiosity to hear the voice of so famous a musician.

'Give me time to arrange my clothes,' said Arion, 'as befits this last act of mine, and tune the strings of my lyre in a manner suitable to one about to address the immortal gods.'

He put on his singing-robes of purple and gold and the garlands of laurel he had won in Sicily. Then he took in his hands the lyre which he had played before kings and queens and tuned each of its strings for the performance of a death song. As he played his instrument and opened his lips in a great song of praise to the gods, gratitude for life and the desire of immortality, the sailors listened enchanted. All but the sternest nearly forgot their wicked purpose.

Then Arion strode to the edge of the deck and gazed down into the calm blue waters. Holding his lyre before him, he sang an address to it, unaccompanied by the sound of strings. 'O lyre,' he sang, 'come with me on my last journey. You who have been the companion of my life shall not be parted from me in death. Together we will make the journey to the dread shores, where the happy souls rest in peace after the turmoil of life. Together we shall charm the dreaded Cerberus who guards the doors of Hades, and we shall not fear to cross

the dark river of death. There we shall see Orpheus himself, whose lyre calmed even the terrible Furies. There we shall meet all the great and famous poets whose music has been silenced on earth. As for those who are sending us on this last solemn journey, the time of their destruction shall surely come!'

So saying, he turned on the sailors with a look of triumph, raised his lyre in the air and sprang overboard into the deep sea. When Arion had sunk beneath the waves, the men tightened sail and made haste to continue on their way. Now, they imagined, they were safe. Their victim was drowned, and none should know of their wickedness, supposing the disappearance of Arion to have been an accident. They could enjoy the fruits of their crime in peace.

But Arion was not drowned. While he had been singing on the deck, the inhabitants of the deep had gathered around to listen – water-nymphs, dolphins, and all the fish of the sea. So when Arion was struggling to keep his head above water, he found himself surrounded by dolphins. He grasped at one of them and pulled himself up on its back. Here he rode safely on the surface of the ocean and was soon brought to the shore. At the place where he landed, a monument was afterwards put up, on which was carved the figure of the poet, lyre in hand, riding upon the dolphin's back. In this way travellers would remember the famous poet whose life had been marvellously preserved.

Arion gazed out to sea after the retreating dolphin, giving thanks to the gods for his deliverance. Then he left the seashore behind him and returned to Corinth. As he journeyed towards the city as swiftly as his legs would take him, he struck the chords of his lyre and raised his voice in a song of happiness and thanksgiving.

Soon he entered the royal palace and was greeted enthusiastically by King Periander.

'My friend and master,' Arion said, 'I have come back to you laden with honour, but not, alas, with treasure. I was victorious in the contest, but evil men have stolen the gifts I had brought for you. I have been stripped of all I own. I have nothing but my lyre, my singing-robes and my fame.'

Periander listened with astonishment and anger while Arion recounted all that had happened to him.

'We must catch these knaves,' he said, 'and punish them as they deserve. Your dolphin must have travelled fast, for no ship has come into harbour from Sicily since you left.'

It was agreed that Arion should remain privately at the palace and that nothing should be said about his return. As soon as the ship came into harbour, Periander had the sailors brought before him. Silently they stood facing the well-guarded figure of the King as he sat on his throne before great embroidered curtains of purple wool.

'I have sent for you,' said the King pleasantly, 'to ask if you saw or heard anything of Arion the musician when you were in Sicily. We await his return.'

The men looked crafty, as their leader stepped forward and said:

'Yes, your majesty, we heard much of his fame in Sicily, and when we set sail for home he was being praised and feasted by all the great ones of the land. He was in the best of health and spirits.'

Then from between the curtains behind the throne stepped Arion, staring in triumph upon the sailors. He appeared exactly as they had last seen him, arrayed in his singing-robes, his wreath of woven laurel, his lyre in his hand. Instantly the sailors fell at the feet of Periander and Arion, groaning and begging for mercy.

'We meant to murder him,' said one. 'But he has become a god and has been saved from drowning. Otherwise he could not appear in living form. May the earth open and take our worthless bodies.'

'Arion is no god,' said Periander, eyeing the wretched men sternly, 'but he has been saved by the help of the gods. My poet has been restored to me. He does not seek your lives, for he is without the spirit of revenge. Better men than you have been tempted to murder by the greed for gold. You shall not be put to death, as you deserve. Instead, when you have restored what you took from your helpless passenger, leave my country, never to return. Find some barbarous land, fitted for thieves and murderers and pass the rest of your days in honest work and true repentance.'

When the sailors had been led away by the guards, Periander turned to Arion and said:

'Fame is good, but the pursuit of it may bring disaster. How fortunate it was that the dolphins have an ear for music. Now let us prepare for the banquet, and after it you shall tune your lyre and sing as you never sang before – not even at the festival in Sicily.'

16

The Fall of Troy

FOR ten years the Greeks had been trying in vain to capture the city of Troy, which lay across the sea. Paris, the son of Priam, King of Troy, had carried off a Greek queen, the beautiful Helen. Her husband, Menelaus, had roused many of the Greek kings and chieftains to gather an army together. They collected many ships and sailed to the coast near Troy. Then they besieged the city and tried to force their way in. For ten long years the war went on. Many brave men were killed on both sides. The Greek warriors began to fear they could never win. But the war came to an end at last, and this is the story of how it happened.

The guardian goddess of Troy was Pallas Athene. There were many statues to her set up in temples in the city, and of these the most famous and the most precious was known as the Palladium. It was thought to have fallen from heaven and so to be a gift from the gods themselves. The Trojans believed that the city could never be taken so long as the Palladium was safe inside its walls.

Then one dark night when all Troy was asleep, and the towers and palaces were lit only by starlight, two bold Greeks, Odysseus and Diomedes, stole silently into Troy, carried off the precious statue and took it back to their camp.

The Greeks well knew how greatly their enemies prized the Palladium.

But in spite of the loss of the statue Troy still held out. The Greeks called a council of war and decided that, since they could not take the city by force, they must do it by trickery. This was the advice of the cunning leader Odysseus. They pretended that they were giving up the fight and sailing home. Some of the ships set sail and left the coast, only to anchor a short distance away behind a nearby island called Tenedos. Some of the Greeks remained behind in their camp on the plains between the sea and the city. Then they built from fir wood a gigantic horse, which they left well within sight of the Trojans. This done, they carried away their tents and equipment and sailed away to join the rest of the fleet moored behind Tenedos. Next morning the Trojan guards reported with amazement that the Greeks were nowhere to be seen. Their camp was broken up, the ships vanished. Great was the rejoicing as the gates of the city were opened and the citizens poured out. They wandered freely over the deserted battle-fields of the past ten years, gazing with wonder at their enemy's old encampment. It all seemed too marvellous to be true.

What excited their liveliest curiosity was the wooden horse. Everyone tried to guess what it was for. Most thought it was a sign for surrender, or a peace offering, or else perhaps an image for the gods to ensure a safe return for the Greek ships,

'Let us take it into the city!' cried some. 'Let us set it up in our market-place as a memorial to our dead and a sign of victory to be shown to our children and grandchildren.'

'Yes,' echoed others. 'Into the city with the horse!'

'Fetch wheels and ropes and drag it in triumph through our gates!'

Then Laocoön, the priest of the sea-god Poseidon, who

was on his way to make a morning sacrifice to the god, raised his hand for silence and called out sternly:

'Are you mad, fellow-Trojans? Never trust the Greeks. This is some trick. Have you fought them for ten years only to be beaten by cunning? I am no coward, but I am afraid of all Greeks, especially when they bring gifts.'

With these words he aimed his spear at the horse's side.

The point pierced it, and a hollow sound came from within. It seemed as if Laocoön had persuaded the Trojans to his way of thinking, for some prepared to destroy the Greek offering there and then.

'He is right,' said someone. 'Let us burn the thing!'

But at that moment a group of Trojans appeared, dragging with them a terrified Greek who had been left behind and had been found hiding among the bushes near the seashore. The man, whose hands had been tied behind his back, was brought before King Priam and the other Trojan leaders.

'Spare my life, I beg,' pleaded the prisoner. 'Or if you will not, then give me a quick and merciful death.'

'We will spare your life,' said the King, 'on condition that you answer our questions truthfully.'

The man promised to tell them all they wanted to know, and his hands were untied.

'I am a Greek,' he said in answer to their questions, 'by name Sinon. The Greeks have sailed for home. The decision to give up the war was taken after long and bitter discussion. It was agreed to make a human sacrifice to the gods on their departure to make sure of a fortunate voyage. Because Odysseus hated me, he persuaded the leaders that I, Sinon, was to be the victim. However, last night I managed to escape and hide near the shore. My countrymen are now my enemies, as they have been yours. All I ask is to be allowed to live among you and become a citizen of Troy – or only a slave, if you so decide.'

Sinon looked so humble and so piteous that no one doubted his words.

'And what,' asked Priam, 'is the purpose of this monstrous image?'

Sinon told the Trojans that the Greeks had left the horse as an offering to the goddess Athena.

'But why did it have to be of this enormous size?'

'Ah,' replied the crafty Sinon, 'it was made huge so that you would not be able to bring it inside your gates. One of our prophets said that if you managed to get the horse inside the city, no one would ever be able to conquer Troy. You would be safe as long as the wooden horse was within your walls.'

All who heard the Greek were deeply impressed. Surely this unfortunate man was speaking the truth. They were beginning to think of ways by which they might drag the monster through the gates of the city when a terrible event occurred – an event which made them hesitate no longer.

Their priest Laocoön, with his two little sons, was on his way to the shore to make his offering to Poseidon when two huge serpents appeared from the sea and advanced directly towards him. All gasped with horror as the scaly creatures wound themselves round the bodies of the boys and crushed them to death. Their father, struggling hopelessly to free the boys, was himself wrapped round the serpents' coils, so that he could no longer breathe and fell lifeless to the ground beside the bodies of the children. A cry of horror went up from the people.

'He has angered the gods,' they said, 'and this is their revenge. He struck the horse with his spear, and they sent the sea-serpents to kill him. Now we know that the image is sacred, and the Greek is speaking the truth.'

Some of the Trojans fetched wheels and ropes and hauled the wooden horse to the gates of the city. Others, meanwhile, took down one of the gateposts and part of the wall which supported it, so as to make room for its passage. Then, with songs of triumph, they pulled it right to the very heart of Troy, where it stood in the market-place towering over the people. They danced about it, strewing flowers before it and throwing garlands about its neck. Then, as evening fell, the people prepared to feast and make merry. Drinking and singing, they roamed about the streets until, worn out with the day's excitements, they went home and slept a sounder sleep than they had enjoyed for ten years. Their enemies had gone, and the wooden horse would keep their city safe.

But Laocoön had been right to mistrust the Greeks, for the horse was no offering to the gods but a means of destruction. Inside its hollow side were a score or more of the bravest of the Greek warriors. They had been waiting there, fully armed, all that day and the whole of the night before. Sinon, who had taken care to hide near the horse, now crept out of the shadows, gave his friends the signal and let them out of their hiding-place. Swiftly they climbed down the rope ladder they had taken inside the horse and made their way to the city gates.

The breach in the wall had been repaired by the Trojans as soon as the horse was inside, and the gates had been closed and barred. But the sentries, fearing no ill, had fallen asleep after their merrymaking, and the Greek warriors had no difficulty in overpowering them. Meanwhile, under cover of night the main body of the Greeks had returned from their shelter behind the island of Tenedos, and were now gathered outside the gates, waiting for their friends to let them in.

Then began the utter destruction of Priam's beautiful city. As the terrified Trojans awoke from sleep, they heard the crackling of flames, the clash of arms and the shouting of the exultant Greeks. Their enemies rushed from street to street, burning, looting and pulling down. The men of Troy hastily buckled on their armour, helped by their panic-stricken women; they went out, sword in hand, to battle with the Greeks. Spears and lances flew through the air. Even the boys fought. As the flames took hold of the lofty buildings, roofs and gables caught fire, and stone towers toppled upon the heads of attackers and defenders alike. Dogs rushed shrieking through the streets, driven mad by the flames. Girls cowered inside the houses, trying to quieten their baby brothers and sisters, until driven out by fire or the enemy.

The Trojans, taken by surprise, were no match for the Greeks. They were put to the sword, while the women were carried off to be slaves. Yet many of the Greeks were slain too. Many of the sons of King Priam were killed or taken prisoner; Priam himself was slain as he took refuge in the temple of Athene.

So ended the great and proud kingdom of Troy, and the city became a smoking ruin, a scene of death and desolation. The Greeks withdrew to their ships and set sail for home, carrying away their slaves and their booty, the treasures of Troy's temples and palaces. Thus ended the ten years' war in a single night.

17

Odysseus and Polyphemus

AFTER the Trojan war the Greek warriors who had taken part in it returned home. Odysseus and his companions set sail in a number of ships and made towards the island of Ithaca, of which he was the ruler. But storms arose and drove the ships off their course. On they went, day after day, getting no nearer home. Before their voyage was done, they had weathered many gales and experienced many adventures. One of the first of these was their visit to the island of the Cyclopes.

These were a tribe of giants, and they were now the sole inhabitants of their island. The word Cyclops means 'the Round-Eyed One'. Each of the giants had only one eye, placed in the middle of his forehead. Not only were the Cyclopes of enormous size, they were rough and shaggy. They were shepherds, living on mutton and on other foods they found on their island. They dwelt in caves.

When Odysseus approached the island, he was in need of rest and refreshment. So he left most of his ships at anchor nearby and sailed his own close in. He and his crew went ashore to spy out the land, taking a large earthenware jar of wine as a present to the natives.

Not far inland they found a deep cave. It belonged to

Polyphemus, one of the strongest and biggest of the Cyclopes. It was this Polyphemus who, when young, had fallen in love with the beautiful sea-nymph Galatea. He had pursued her, singing rough songs in his huge, rumbling voice. But this only frightened her. Then he would sit for hours among his enormous rams, playing on a pipe he had made of a hundred reeds. This, too, had displeased the nymph.

She was, indeed, in love with a handsome young shepherd called Acis. One day Acis was lying in the mouth of a cave under the cliffs wooing Galatea with soft words, when they heard the raucous tones of the Cyclops bawling songs of lamentation as he sat on a promontory near the sea. He was far enough away, but his voice carried like the noise of thunder among the mountains.

Then Polyphemus, restless and unhappy, strode to the top of a rock, where his sheep, to which he paid small attention, followed him. Then he threw down his staff, the trunk of a young pine tree, took out his reed-pipe and began to play.

Suddenly, casting his eye about him, he caught sight of Galatea in the arms of Acis. This was too much for the lovesick giant. He jumped to his feet and roared out:

'Aha! I see you, cruel maiden! You are happy with your shepherd, but I will make sure this is the last time you and he make love together!'

The sound of the Cyclops's voice so terrified Galatea that she jumped up in alarm and sprang into the sea. Only a ripple was left to show where she had dived in.

Acis, too, rose up in alarm and tried to run away. But Polyphemus, with huge strides, followed him, tearing off a boulder from the mountainside as he did so. This he threw with all his force at the retreating shepherd. The giant's aim was good, and Acis was buried beneath the rock.

But the gods took pity on him. From the earth there gushed

first red blood, then muddy water. Then the rock split open, and a tall green reed rose up. Next a clear, sparkling spring appeared, the river god standing in its cool waters. So was born a new river, and to this day it is called the Acis. As for Polyphemus, he left that country and went back to his own people. He never took a wife, nor did he ever again play on his pipes or sing love-songs. Silent and disconsolate, he brooded alone in his cave or among his flocks in the hills.

When Odysseus and his companions came to the cave, the owner was away, tending his sheep. They entered it and found it stocked with fine, fat sheep, lambs and kids, cheeses and bowls of milk. Presently the master of the cave returned Odysseus and his men were well hidden inside the cave. From their hiding-place, they saw Polyphemus drive his flocks in, throw down a pile of firewood and then close the mouth of the cave by rolling into it a huge boulder. This he did with scarcely an effort, but it would have taken twenty oxen to move it. Next Polyphemus sat down upon a stout wooden stool and milked the sheep. He set aside part of the milk to make cheese, and the rest he kept in a bowl for his supper.

At last he turned round. With his glaring eye he saw the strangers – Odysseus and his sailors hiding in the rear of the cave.

'Who are you?' he roared in a monstrous voice. 'And what are you doing here?'

'We are Greeks, sir,' answered Odysseus respectfully. 'We have taken part in the long war against Troy. Now we are returning home, and our ship has been driven on to this island. We seek rest, food and shelter. In the name of the gods who are above us all, we beg the favour of your hospitality.'

The giant made no reply but slowly rose from his stool and approached the men. Then with his huge, brawny arms and enormous hands he seized two of them and flung them crash-

187

ing against the wall of the cave. The others were horrified to see their luckless companions murdered in cold blood. They were still more horrified to see the giant devour them, tearing them apart with his bare hands. Then Polyphemus washed down his meal with a bowl of milk, stretched himself out and lay on the floor of the cave to sleep.

'Kill him, master,' said one of the sailors in a hoarse whisper. 'He's asleep. Stick your sword into his heart before he can wake.'

'I am sorely tempted to do it,' answered Odysseus. 'But if we kill him now, we shall never escape. We shall die here miserably once we have eaten all the cheese and drunk all the milk. How can we ever hope to shift that enormous rock and get out of the cave alive? We are imprisoned unless the giant himself moves the rock.'

Sadly the sailors agreed that Odysseus was right. They made a meal of cheese and milk and lay down to sleep.

Next morning Polyphemus stretched his great hairy body, yawned and rose to his feet. Then he seized two more of Odysseus's shrinking companions and served them as he had served the others, devouring their lifeless bodies with relish. When he had finished his grisly breakfast, he rolled back the rock and drove his sheep and goats out to pasture. Before he left, he was careful to push the rock back into position, so as to keep his visitors imprisoned until his return.

While he was away, Odysseus sat down to work out a plan for getting the better of their enemy and escaping from their dreadful prison. He made his men sharpen the end of a huge wooden pole which the giant had brought into the cave as a staff and hardened the point in the fire. Then they hid it under the straw at the back of the cave.

Towards nightfall the giant returned as before with his flock, milked them and prepared supper. Once more he seized two of Odysseus's companions and made his supper of them. Then Odysseus came forward and offered him a bowl of wine.

'Drink it, Cyclops,' he said. 'It will taste good and refresh you after a meal of human flesh.'

Polyphemus grabbed the bowl of wine and greedily drank it down at a single gulp.

Odysseus gave him more. The giant grinned to show his pleasure.

'That is good,' he said. 'Thank you for this. I will keep you till the end and not eat you until I have eaten all the others. What is your name?'

'My name,' answered the cunning Odysseus, 'is Noman.'

Drowsy with the strong wine, Polyphemus was soon fast asleep, snoring like distant thunder. At once Odysseus and four chosen companions fetched out the sharpened pole from under the straw and made it red-hot in the embers of the fire. It burned and glowed and crackled. Then the five of them stood above the sleeping giant, raised the pole high in the air and, at a signal from Odysseus, drove it deep into the giant's only eye. They twirled it in the socket as a carpenter twirls his gimlet. As the monster, howling with pain, woke and jumped to his feet, they sprang out of reach, joining their companions at the farther end of the cave. Polyphemus, groaning and bellowing, lunged blindly here and there, knocking himself against the walls and stumbling over boulders, arousing the frightened animals with his cries and making them bleat piteously. Never had such a din been heard in the island of the Cyclopes. The other giants from neighbouring caves came running towards the dwelling of Polyphemus, shouting:

'What is the matter, Polyphemus, that you bawl out in this way and wake us from our slumbers?'

'I am hurt,' he called. 'I have been blinded and I shall die of the pain.'

'Who has hurt you?' they called.

'Noman,' replied Polyphemus. 'Noman has hurt me.'

'Then if no man has hurt you,' they answered, 'it must be the will of the gods, and we can do nothing for you. We cannot alter the will of Zeus.'

Then the other giants departed and left Polyphemus to his groaning.

Next morning the Cyclops rolled away the stone from the mouth of the cave to let out his flocks. He could not see, so, to be sure that Odysseus and his men did not escape, he stood by the wall of the entrance to make sure that they did not pass him. But cunning Odysseus had made his men yoke the sheep together, three by three, using strands of willow that had been brought into the cave to make baskets for the giant's cheeses. Under the belly of the middle sheep hung a Greek, clinging to the animal's fleece. Polyphemus felt the backs and sides of the outermost sheep, in case the Greeks should be riding on their backs, but he did not think of feeling their bellies. So all the Greeks passed out of the giant's cave. Odysseus himself came out last.

As soon as the men were clear of the cave, they jumped down from under the sheep and made for the boat, driving as many of the sheep as possible before them. They intended to keep them on board for food during the voyage. As soon as they were safely in the boat, they pushed out to sea.

When they were a safe distance from the shore, Odysseus, standing on the deck, looked towards the sightless giant near the water's edge and called out:

'Cyclops, the gods have punished you for your vile cruelty towards a helpless band of Greeks. Know you, Cyclops, that it was I, Odysseus of Ithaca, who planned and carried out the act which blinded you and gave us our freedom.'

For answer the enraged Polyphemus wrenched a mighty rock from the ground, raised it on high with his two mighty arms and hurled it with all his strength towards the voice he had heard. The rock rose high in the air, narrowly missed the ship's mainmast and crashed into the water just beyond the vessel. So huge was the wave thus caused that the ship was driven back towards the island and beached itself once more in the sand. The men were hard put to it to drive the ship once more out to sea. Once more Odysseus was about to address the monster, but his friends persuaded him to wait till they were farther from the land. As soon as they were at a safe distance, the Greeks raised their voices in a great shout, to let Polyphemus know that they had escaped his vengeance.

Then they hoisted sail, bent their backs to the oars and made off as fast as they could to rejoin the other ships.

18

Odysseus and Circe

ODYSSEUS and his men sailed on, caring only to reach their homes on the isle of Ithaca. When there was a good breeze, they hoisted the sails and sped over the blue waves. When there was no wind, they bent their backs to the oars and pulled sturdily. The voyage was long and weary. They had many times been driven off their course, and Odysseus decided to ask for the help of the god Aeolus, in whose keeping were all the winds that blow. So he steered his ship towards the island where Aeolus lived, and the other ships followed. Next day they put in at the harbour, and Odysseus went up to the palace of King Aeolus. The King and his family were feasting. The traveller was hospitably entertained, and next morning Aeolus gave him a leather bag whose mouth was tied with a thong. It bulged with all the winds. Odysseus was told to release only the west wind, and this would drive his ship home. He thanked the King, rejoined his men, weighed anchor and set off. He kept the bag beside him, and himself managed the helm. Then he carefully opened the bulging bag and let out only the west wind. Gradually the sails filled, and the ship bounded over the waves.

For several days the ship rode on. Odysseus alone managed

the helm, so fearful was he that they might go off course. At length he became weary and, almost within sight of his native land, he lay down on the deck and fell fast asleep. The moon came out and shone on the sleeping form of the leader and on the bulging leather bag he kept beside him.

The sailors gathered round and began talking in undertones.

'I'd like to know what the old man has in that bag,' said one of them.

'Mark my words,' said another, 'that King – Aeolus, wasn't it? – gave him some treasure to take home, and that's what's in the bag.'

'Yes, shouldn't wonder. He's going to keep it all to himself. We'll ask him for a share of it.'

'First, let's look inside and make sure what it is. Gold and silver and precious stones, I shouldn't wonder.'

'Come on then. Undo the bag. Do it quietly or you'll wake him.'

Then the sailor nearest to Odysseus drew out a sharp knife and cut the cord that bound the neck of the bag. Instantly all the other winds rushed out with a mighty roar, and Odysseus awoke to find the ship tossing madly in all directions.

'Fools!' he cried. 'What have you done? You have ruined everything, and we shall be destroyed by storms. Quick, lower the sails. Get to your stations and man the oars.'

But it was too late. Already the sails were filled with a great wind from the north-east. The ship rocked and pitched. The men had strength only to lower the smaller of the sails. They were driven violently back towards the island of Aeolus, which they had left only a few days earlier.

Odysseus made the men take the ship into harbour, and once more he sought the help of Aeolus. But the King spoke to him sternly.

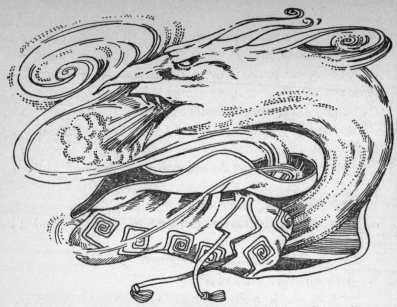

'No,' he said. 'I dare not help you further. The gods are against you. This is proved by your falling asleep when at the helm and allowing your men to act recklessly. You must continue your journey without my help.'

Once more they set out, but now the winds failed and the sails hung idly, flapping against the masts. The men were obliged to use the oars. At length, weary and discouraged, they put in at the island of the Laestrygonians in search of food and water. These were a race of cannibal giants, as savage and barbarous as the Cyclopes. Some of the ships went right into the harbour, but Odysseus wisely remained in open water outside. As soon as the giants saw the ships, they seized great rocks and hurled them over the cliffs, smashing two or three of the ships to fragments. As rock after rock crashed down on the decks, the sailors could do nothing except scramble into the water and make for the shore as best they could. Here the cruel Laestrygonians speared them from above, so that none was left alive. Seeing that he could do nothing to help them, Odysseus gave orders to his crew to row for their lives and get as far away as possible from the accursed island.

In course of time the ship reached the island of Aeaea, where lived the enchantress Circe, bright-haired daughter of the sun god. Here on the shore Odysseus and his men rested for two days. There was no sign of life on the island, so Odysseus climbed a high hill not far inland to spy out the country. He saw no human habitations except one. This was a fair palace standing in a glade among trees in the centre of the island. He returned to the shore and told his men what he had discovered. Then he divided the party into two – one under his own command, the other under the command of Eurylochus. The two leaders drew lots as to which should go first and make himself known at the palace. The lot fell to Eurylochus, who with his men set off towards the centre of the island. Odysseus and his party awaited their return.

When Eurylochus and his men reached the grove where stood the palace, they were surrounded by lions and wolves. In terror some of them turned to run. Others drew their spears and prepared to fight. But to their amazement the beasts were all tame, fawning upon them and licking their hands and faces, as a dog greets his master after a long absence.

The reason was this. The beasts had all been men, but they had been changed by the magic power of the enchantress Circe. They had the forms of lions and wolves, but their hearts and minds were still those of men.

Encouraged by this, the party approached the gates of the palace. Within they heard the sound of sweet music and of women's voices. Then the bright-haired queen herself came out and beckoned them inside. All went in except Eurylochus. He was afraid and waited outside the gate.

Circe bade the men be seated at a long table in her hall. Then she had servants place before them delicate food and strong wine. The men feasted and drank as they had never done before. As they did so, Circe walked back and forth before her great loom, weaving a cloth of rich dyes and mysterious design, singing to herself in her high, unearthly voice.

Then, when she saw that her guests were half asleep with eating and drinking, she took up a golden wand of delicate workmanship and touched each of them lightly on the shoulder, muttering an incantation in some strange tongue. Instantly each of the sailors was turned into a pig. Grunting and jostling each other, they ran about the hall. Their flapping ears, bristly skins and curved tusks were those of pigs, but their hearts and minds remained their own. Circe summoned her swineherds who, with sharp sticks drove the squealing beasts into sties at the rear of the palace. Here they were penned in and fed on beechnuts and acorns and the swill from the kitchens.

Seeing all this, Eurylochus, in fear and sorrow, sped back to the shore to tell their leader what had happened.

'Where are your companions?' asked Odysseus as soon as he saw Eurylochus. 'What has become of my men?'

'Oh, master,' cried Eurylochus with tears in his eyes, 'a terrible thing has befallen them!' Then, with horror and despair making his tale more piteous, he described all he had seen.

At once Odysseus set off alone to see what he could do to deliver his men from their terrible captivity. In vain Eurylochus pleaded with him not to go, or at least to take some trusted companion. But Odysseus, as brave as he was cunning, set off alone.

Half-way to the palace he met a young man of pleasing

appearance who greeted him and begged speech with him.

'You are the famous Odysseus, I know,' said the youth, 'and you are on your way home after serving the Greeks at Troy.'

Then the young man said he was Hermes, messenger of the gods, who had bidden him find out Odysseus and be of service to him on his journey.

'Circe,' he told Odysseus, 'is an enchantress of great power and she has changed your men into beasts, just as you have been told. She will do the same to you, and I advise you to get as far from her as you can and put as many sea miles as possible between you and her island.'

'No,' said Odysseus firmly. 'I brought the men here, and it is for me to do what I can to rescue them.'

'Very well,' said Hermes. 'Since you are determined to face the enchantress, listen to me carefully. Gather some of this herb you see growing about you – the one with the black root and the white flower, called moly. Keep it with you when you encounter the witch, and it will protect you against her enchantments. When she attempts to bewitch you, you must rush at her with your sword drawn and make as if to cut her throat. When she is at your mercy, she will agree to do all you ask. Now do as I say, and may the gods protect you.'

Odysseus thanked the young man and went on his way. He boldly entered the courtyard of the palace and stood before the entrance. Circe, the bright-haired daughter of the sun god, her heart dark with mischief, welcomed him in and treated him courteously, bidding him to be seated at her table. Servants brought him food and wine, and she entertained him by singing before her loom. Then, when he had feasted and drunk, she stepped swiftly towards him, touched him on the shoulder with her golden wand and said in a shrill, inhuman voice:

'There, stranger! Now go to the sty and eat with your fellow-swine!'

But Odysseus grew no long bristles, nor did he grunt and squeal. Instead, he drew his sharp sword, brandished it over the enchantress and stared into her face with a look of fury. The sorceress was beaten. She went down on her knees, raised her hands towards him and begged to be allowed to live.

'Very well,' said Odysseus. 'On one condition. Repeat after me this oath.'

Then she swore to restore Odysseus's companions to their former manly shape, entertain them hospitably and without doing them further harm, and finally let them go in peace and security.

'You are Odysseus,' she said when she had sworn the oath. 'Hermes came and told me to expect you. I will release your sailors and you shall all be entertained at my palace for as long as you wish to stay.'

At once the men who had been turned into pigs were changed back into men. They looked even younger and more handsome than before. Odysseus went back to the shore to summon the others to the palace. Eurylochus was still afraid and wished to remain behind, but Odysseus would not let him.

'Come,' he said. 'All is now safe. Let us eat and drink at the queen's expense and pass our days in ease and pleasure.'

Circe did all that she had promised. Odysseus and his men were royally entertained, and for many days they stayed with her. They roamed the island, playing games among themselves or swimming in the blue sea as if they had no cares in the world. They feasted and drank to their hearts' content, and Circe practised no further enchantments upon them. It seemed as if Odysseus had forgotten his home and the purpose of his voyage.

At last Eurylochus and some of the others reminded him that they had wives and children who had been waiting for their return for many long years. Odysseus agreed to bid farewell to the enchantress. She parted from him with tears of farewell in her eyes, giving him instructions for the next stage of his journey. In particular she warned him of the dangers that awaited him when he should pass the island of the Sirens. Then one bright morning when the wind was favourable, Odysseus made sacrifice to the gods and boarded his ship. The men hoisted sail, weighed anchor and watched the island of Aeaea grow smaller in the distance.

Not long afterwards Odysseus knew that the ship was approaching the Sirens, so he ordered everything to be done as Circe had advised. The island, he was told, was surrounded by treacherous and jagged rocks, on which a ship might be wrecked and a swimmer torn to pieces. On the shores of this island lay the Sirens, maidens of great beauty not unlike the mermaids of later legends. As they combed their long, flowing hair, they sang songs of such unearthly sweetness that no man who heard them could resist their magic. Some played on stringed instruments made from great sea-shells. All raised their voices in strains of unrivalled harmony, not heard elsewhere by human ears. Many was the good ship which had been steered on to the rocks by men unable to sail past the Sirens' island; many were the young sailors who had leaped into the sea and been torn to pieces on the hidden rocks, so that whitening bones and fragments of wreckage were to be seen all along the shore as a warning to desperate and foolish mariners. Those relics should have spoken plainly to all, but Circe had urged Odysseus to take no risks.

He told the men to fill their ears with wax, so that they should not hear the song of the Sirens. As for him, he stood with his back to the mainmast and his eyes towards the shore, while his men bound him to the mast with ropes. On no account were they to obey him if he should tell them to release him. He was to remain bound to the mast so long as the island was within sight and sound.

No sooner were these preparations complete than they came in sight of the shore, edged with the bones of sailors and tall ships. On the beaches lay the Sirens, some combing their hair, others plucking the strings of their lyres. All sang. The mariners saw everything but heard nothing. Their leader alone was allowed to listen to the ravishing strains of their music, as they beckoned to him with song and gesture to come and taste the joys of their island. He was seized with an overwhelming desire to sail nearer. Sweating and straining, he heaved at the ropes till they cut into his flesh and he cried out in pain. Then he signalled to the men to come and cut the cords. But they obeyed his earlier command and brought more ropes to lash him still faster to the mast. It seemed as if the mast would crack with the strain. Then at last, out of breath from his exertions, he relaxed and leaned back, his ears filled with the Sirens' music, till it grew fainter and fainter as the ship swung past the fatal shore and the gleaming beaches, and the maidens and their songs were lost in the distance.

When the place was no more than a speck on the horizon, Odysseus ordered the crew to release him and take the wax from their ears. Thus one more danger was passed on the long voyage back to Ithaca from the ruined city of Troy.

19

Scylla and Charybdis

BEFORE Odysseus left the island of the enchantress Circe, she warned him of a further danger they would encounter. Soon they would have to pass through a narrow strait between high cliffs. On one side was a whirlpool named Charybdis. It boiled and hissed and threw up great spouts of foam. As the angry water swirled over the bottomless chasm, it sought, like some devouring monster, to suck into its gulf any boat or ship that passed too close. Many poor sailors and fine vessels, passing too near the dreadful whirlpool, had been dragged into its depths and lost for ever. But if a ship sailed too close to the opposite shore of the strait, it ran into an equally terrible danger. This was the monster Scylla, who lived in a cave high up in the cliffs opposite the whirlpool. Scylla had been a beautiful maiden, but Circe had changed her into a snaky creature with six heads. In each of her mouths stood two rows of sharp teeth, and it was her habit to reach down her serpent necks whenever a ship passed within reach and seize as many of the crew as she could. She carried them into her cave and devoured them with hideous delight. Many brave men had met their end in this manner.

Odysseus's ship had not long been sailing from Circe's island when there rose into view the spray and steam from the

whirlpool Charybdis. Odysseus had warned them of this danger, and they now became panic-stricken, so that the blades of the oars fell upon the water, and they could no longer row.

'Take heart, men!' cried Odysseus. 'This danger is no worse than what we faced in the cave of Polyphemus. I brought you safely out of that, and we shall live to tell our children of how we escaped from the whirlpool. Keep close into the farther shore and row your hardest.'

So the sailors took heart, gripped their oars and pulled hard for the entrance to the strait, steering close in to the shore farthest from the whirlpool. But Odysseus had not dared to tell them of the peril that lay in wait on this side. If he had told them of Scylla, he was afraid they would lose heart altogether, drop their oars and hide themselves below deck. They must be made to row hard through the narrow passage, come what might.

Circe had forbidden Odysseus to arm himself, for, she said, the monster was irresistible. With her six heads and writhing, snaky necks she could never be destroyed. But this command was too much for a fighter, so Odysseus buckled on his armour, took up two spears and stood on the prow of the ship to get a sight of the monster. In vain he strained his eyes, trying to discover her cave high in the cliff.

Nearer and nearer sailed the ship towards the narrowest part of the passage. As it reached the whirlpool, the men did not flinch, but rowed hard, as Odysseus had told them. They felt the pull of the water, and as they neared the deadly gulf, they could see right down its spinning sides to the sand and rocks beneath. They shuddered, and the steersman held his course near the farther cliffs. It was then that Scylla thrust her six heads out of the cave and seized six of the sailors with her horrible fangs. Their companions were terrified to see them raised screaming into the air, struggling hopelessly to free themselves from Scylla's grip. Their efforts were in vain. Writhing and screaming and calling upon their leader and the gods to help them for the last time, they vanished into the cave, where the ravening beast devoured them. This was the most horrible event which took place during the whole of Odysseus's journey.

Sad at heart, but thankful to be out of reach of Scylla and Charybdis, Odysseus and his men sailed out of the narrow waters into the open sea. Soon they could make out on the horizon the island of the sun god, of which Circe had told Odysseus. She had warned him on no account to land there, however tempted he might be, for the island was sacred to the golden cattle of the sun. It was death to any man who should injure these cattle. Nearer and nearer they came to the lovely island. Soon they could see its golden sands and hospitable coves with vines and olives coming almost down to the water's edge. Further inland were rich meadows where the golden cattle browsed peacefully, now and again raising their heads to low contentedly.

The tired eyes of the sailors rested hungrily on these sights. Sternly Odysseus told them they might not land but must sail on.

Then the men began to grumble and protest. Angrily Eurylochus spoke out:

'Odysseus, are you a man of flesh and blood or a stone statue? After our terrible journey between the whirlpool and the six-headed monster are we to have no rest?'

'It is the command of the gods,' said Odysseus sternly.

'Night is coming on,' Eurylochus replied. 'Let us anchor here at least till morning. We cannot struggle on through the darkness. How if a storm should arise and smash us to pieces or drive us back into the cruel straits?'

All the crew loudly supported Eurylochus, and with a heart full of foreboding Odysseus was forced to consent. But he made them swear an oath to the immortal gods that they would on no account touch the golden cattle, the sacred cattle of the sun. So they beached the ship, drew water from a clear spring and sat down on the shore to eat the food they had brought. Then at last, overcome by weariness and by grief at the loss of their six friends, they fell asleep.

A little after midnight the sky suddenly became covered with a thick cloud, so that the stars were blotted out and a fierce storm arose. It was just as Eurylochus had feared. Odysseus roused his men, and together they dragged the ship high on shore to be out of reach of the rising storm, for he feared it might be dashed to pieces. The wind had changed and for a whole month it blew hard from the wrong quarter. They dared not put to sea.

Before long they had eaten all the provisions in the ship and began to snare birds and catch fish to keep themselves alive. It was a sparse diet, for the weather made it hard to get enough of either birds or fish. Some of the men began to think of the fat beasts that would be theirs to roast if only they dare break their oath not to harm the golden cattle.

Odysseus, perplexed and anxious, went to a quiet place away from the others in order to pray to the gods for help. Sleep fell upon him, and before he awoke, Eurylochus had given his companions bad counsel.

'Friends,' he said, 'we have sworn not to touch the cattle. But if we do not, we shall starve. No man could live on what we are able to catch. We are ill with hunger. Before we have not strength enough left, let us kill the fattest of the cows and make a sacrifice to the gods. Then, if we reach home, we can build a temple to the sun god as an offering for our safe return and to calm his anger at our disobedience. But even if he wrecks our ship in revenge, it would be better to die a quick death by drowning than slowly starve within sight and sound of food.'

All agreed, and without further argument they killed two or three of the fattest of the cows with their spears and roasted the flesh. As soon as it was done, they sacrificed part of the meat to the gods. The rest they fell upon and began to devour.

Odysseus awoke and sniffed the delicious smell. He began to groan, for he guessed what had happened. At once the sun god knew of the outrage that had been done to the golden beasts that were his greatest joy on earth. He went to the throne of Zeus, father of the gods, and asked him to punish with a thunderbolt those who had committed the crime. Thus the punishment of the sailors was assured.

Odysseus, meanwhile, hurried to the place from which came the savoury smell. He bitterly reproached his companions for breaking their oath. But it was too late. They had already begun to feast on the forbidden flesh. Then a strange thing happened. The skins of the slain animals began to creep and writhe, and an unearthly moaning was heard from the lumps of flesh roasting in the fire. Odysseus shook his head sadly. He knew that these were signs of the anger of the gods. For six days he and his crew waited, until the last of the meat was consumed. Then the wind changed, and Odysseus ordered his men to push the ship down to the beach and hoist sail. When all were aboard, they put out to sea, and before long the island was lost to view.

When the ship was in open water, a black cloud appeared overhead. Sea and sky grew dark, until it was impossible to make out which was which. Suddenly the storm struck. The anger of the gods was swift. A hurricane tore the mast from its stays. It crashed down upon the steersman, whose lifeless body rolled into the dark water. The rest of the crew were washed from the deck. But Odysseus still clung firmly to what was left of the ship, until it was wholly stripped of its tackle by the fury of the gale. When the ship was torn to pieces and the wreckage scattered on the sea, Odysseus clung to a stout spar and prayed to the gods for deliverance. He alone, of all the ship's company, had survived the storm. Then to his horror he saw that once more the wind had changed, and he was being driven helplessly back towards the strait where Scylla and Charybdis lurked. Nearer and nearer he was tossed towards the dreaded whirlpool. Just as the spar to which he clung was about to be sucked into the spinning gulf, he raised himself with all his strength and leaped towards a tree whose branches overhung the pool. There he clung, awaiting death from exhaustion, or deliverance by some miracle sent by the gods. Then the whirlpool subsided for a time, and once more Odysseus saw his fragment of wreckage tossed upon the waters. Hastily ripping part of a branch from the tree to which he was clinging, he sprang into the water and struggled back on to the spar. Then with his home-made paddle he pushed himself as far from the spot as he could, and soon he was once more free of the perils of the strait.

Odysseus was now entirely alone. Across the waves he battled, resolute in his determination to survive all dangers and return to the home he had left so many years before. Just as he was beginning to despair of ever reaching land, he sighted an island. This was the dwelling of the sea-nymph Calypso. He swam ashore and was sighted by Calypso's maidens, who led him to the home of their mistress. Here he was given fresh clothes, food and wine. When he had rested, Odysseus told the nymph all his adventures, and she bade him stay with her till he was ready to continue his journey. He told her he was anxious to set out without delay but

Calypso enjoyed the company of the weather-beaten traveller with his endless tales of storm and peril. She entertained him for many months at her palace, with its gardens and vineyards, bright with the song of birds and the glitter of stream and fountain.

At last the gods took a hand. Zeus had determined that Odysseus should reach home after such long and weary travels, so he sent his messenger Hermes to tell the nymph to say goodbye to her guest and speed him on his way.

Accordingly, with sadness in her heart, but obedient to the gods, Calypso gave Odysseus the means to make a raft. She gave him also a favourable wind and bade him farewell. He thanked her for her kindness, hoisted the sail he had made, saw that he had enough provisions for the journey and set out.

But Odysseus had not weathered his last storm. For many days he fared well, and then a sudden squall struck the raft and broke the mast in half. Odysseus and his craft were driven hopelessly hither and thither, with no sail to bear them on. But he did not give up hope, and a sea-nymph, taking pity on his plight, alighted on the raft in the form of a cormorant. She bade him be of stout heart and gave him a girdle. She told him to bind it round himself in case he found it necessary to abandon the raft and take to the water. This girdle would bear him up even in the stormiest of seas. Then the nymph spread her wings and flew off, leaving Odysseus to fare onwards as best the gods would allow.

20

The Homecoming of Odysseus

ALONE on the wide sea, Odysseus was borne along until a storm arose and his raft began to break up. So, trusting to the protection of Athene and to the girdle given him by the sea-nymph, he dived into the water. He struggled on until, towards the evening, he made out the rocky coast of an island. Half-dead with weariness, he succeeded in scrambling ashore. He gave thanks to the gods for his deliverance, then made himself a bed of dry leaves and fell asleep.

The land where Odysseus was cast up was the island of Scheria, where dwelt a race of sea kings known as the Phaeacians. They were a peaceable people devoted to sailing. Their king was Alcinous, and he ruled his people justly and kindly. On the morning of Odysseus's arrival, his daughter Nausicaa went down to the shore with her maidens and came upon the sleeping hero.

Nausicaa gave Odysseus fresh clothes and brought him back to her father's palace. Here he was given food and wine and was hospitably entertained. But he longed to be on his way, and at last the Phaeacians put him aboard a ship and took him back to his own country of Ithaca. When they reached the harbour, Odysseus was asleep, so they laid him down on the shore and sailed away.

When Odysseus awoke, he had no idea where he was. He

had been away from home for twenty years, and he could not remember what it looked like. But Athene appeared to him in the form of a young shepherd. Odysseus asked the shepherd where he was. The shepherd told him he was in Ithaca, and went on to relate the sorry tale of what had been going on in his absence:

'It is twenty years since our ruler Odysseus left the island to fight in the war against Troy. I was not born then, but my parents have told me everything. Our king left behind his wife, Penelope, and their baby son Telemachus. For ten years the war went on, and ten years have now passed since it ended. But Odysseus has not come home, and not long ago the prince, Telemachus, set off to see if he could get news of his father. For although few suppose him to be alive, no news has yet to come of his death.

'About three years ago a great crowd of princes and nobles, some from Ithaca and some from neighbouring islands, came here and began to seek the hand of the Queen in marriage. So far she has put them off, saying that nothing will make her take another husband, at least until she has proof of Odysseus's death.

'They are rude, unmannerly men, these suitors. They have taken up residence in the city, and daily go and feast at the palace at the Queen's expense. Her best sheep and calves have all been slaughtered and her fields laid waste. Odysseus's old, faithful servants, his herdsmen and reapers, have been insulted and made wretched by the insolent suitors and their followers. In grief and despair Odysseus's mother has died, and his father Laertes has gone to live by himself in a cottage outside the city. The whole land is miserable, and the Queen grieves all day to think of the joyful times before her husband sailed for Troy. All wonder if he will ever return; but as the years go on, hope grows less.

'Daily the suitors become more pressing. They urge her to choose one of them as a husband. She tells them she cannot even think of another husband till she has finished the great cloth she is weaving on her loom. Every day the cloth grows a little, but every night, when all are asleep, she unweaves what she has done during the day. No one can tell how long she can keep the suitors waiting by this trick. Some day they will discover it.'

On hearing this sad story, Odysseus at once began to think how he might be revenged on these insolent visitors. He must not reveal himself, or the suitors would assuredly plot to kill him. So the goddess Athene threw over him the guise of a wretched old beggar, ragged and dirty, and in this guise he set out to see for himself how things were.

When Odysseus was nearing the city, he was kindly received by one of his own old servants. This was the swineherd Eumaeus, who lived in a hut and looked after the pigs belonging to the Queen. His life was made miserable by the greed and brutality of the suitors. But he remained his old master's faithful servant.

It was the rule in Ithaca that strangers, even beggars, should be kindly welcomed, and Eumaeus gave Odysseus shelter in his hut. He did not know, of course, that it was his own master he was caring for.

Now it so happened that just at this time Telemachus returned home from his journey in search of news. He had visited some of the kings who had returned to their islands after the fall of Troy. They had told him nothing positive about his father, except that he had taken a ship from Troy and set out for home. He had been driven off course, and little had been seen of him since. Yet none had heard of his death, and there was a strong feeling that one day he would return. However, Telemachus dared not show himself openly at the palace for fear the suitors might do him harm. Accordingly the old swineherd Eumaeus was sent to tell Penelope privately of her son's homecoming and see how matters stood at the palace.

As soon as Eumaeus was out of sight and hearing, Athene appeared to Odysseus and told him to reveal himself to his son. Great was the astonishment of the young man to see the ragged beggar transformed into his true self – a vigorous, upstanding and weather-beaten hero. He wept tears of joy on learning that the man was no other than his father, whom he had not seen since he was an infant. Odysseus explained that his disguise was the work of the goddess.

Father and son talked of the important matter of how they were to be revenged on the horde of suitors. Odysseus told Telemachus to return to the palace and mix with the suitors. He was to take his rightful place as head of the household and was to be courteous to strangers and beggars, as had been the custom of old. He was to say nothing of the return of his father. Odysseus, meanwhile, would come to the palace disguised once more as a beggar and would be received in the great hall and be given food and wine. In those days it was customary for wandering beggars to be received in this way, entertaining the great ones in the hall with songs or stories in exchange for their hospitality. Odysseus warned his son that the suitors would insult him and treat him with contempt, but the young man was not to interfere. He must use his father with the respect and courtesy due to any wayfarer, and must not show that he had any special interest in him. In this way the guests would suspect nothing, but simply imagine that Odysseus was an ordinary traveller, begging his way from place to place.

So next morning Telemachus went to the palace and greeted his mother Penelope. She was overjoyed to see him, as were all the servants, especially Eurycleia, who had been the nurse of Telemachus and of his father before him. Telemachus told Penelope that he had no real news of Odysseus, except that he had been sighted somewhere on his travels and that nowhere had his death been reported. He bade her continue in hope.

Eumaeus, meanwhile, led his guest, the ragged old beggar, to the town. On their way they met a man named Melanthius, who had been Odysseus's goatherd. He was on his way to the palace with the best of the goats, to be slaughtered for the suitors' feast next day. Melanthius was rude to old Eumaeus and insulted the beggar, mocking his raggedness and his hungry looks. Odysseus, who could easily have knocked the goatherd down at a blow, swallowed his insults calmly. He wished no one to suspect that he was no beggar but a man of strength and vigour. But the meeting with the goatherd helped him to see how badly things had gone in Ithaca while he had been away.

When Eumaeus and Odysseus reached the gates of the palace, Eumaeus went inside, to be courteously received by the young master, Telemachus. Odysseus, a little way behind him, noticed an ancient hound, half starved and covered with sores, lying on a dunghill. It was Odysseus's own hound Argus, who had not seen his master for twenty years. But the dog recognized him, raised his head in greeting and wagged his tail. Then he fell back dead. It was as if he had lived only to see once again his beloved master.

When Odysseus reached the door of the great hall, the suitors were gathered at the tables, eating, drinking and laughing together. Telemachus told Odysseus to be seated and sent him a dish of food to eat and a cup of wine. Then he told him that the laws of hospitality allowed him to go boldly from guest to guest asking for money or other gifts. Odysseus did as his son bade him. Some of the suitors treated him kindly, but Antinous, the boldest and most insolent of them, jeered at them for so treating a mere beggar. Then he picked up a footstool and flung it at the old man. It hit him on the shoulder. Odysseus did nothing, but submitted humbly to the blow. Telemachus, his cheeks reddening, his eyes flashing, longed to avenge this insult offered to the King in his own hall. But he checked himself, remembering what his father had told him.

Then Eumaeus took leave of Telemachus and went off to see to the wine. The feasting and revelry continued. Odysseus remained to look after the braziers of live charcoal which had been brought in to warm the suitors after nightfall. Some of the suitors took to insulting the old man, but neither he nor his son answered them. Their taunts only made the thought of revenge the sweeter. The guests brought out presents for Penelope. She showed herself at the feast, and they urged her to hurry and make up her mind which of them she was going to marry. At length, full of food and wine, the suitors stumbled off to their houses, drunkenly bidding one another goodnight and singing snatches of song.

Then Odysseus talked with Penelope, but he dared not yet tell her who he was. He bade her be of good heart and act courageously in the trials before her, for he promised her that Odysseus was living and would suddenly return. She thanked him and wished him goodnight, telling the old nurse Eurycleia to see to his needs. Eurycleia took a basin of warm water and a cloth and washed his feet, as was the custom. In so doing, she noticed the scar on one of his legs. She had known it ever since the days when she had had charge of him as a little boy. In her excitement she overturned the bowl of water, and tears came into her eyes. But she said nothing and gave no sign of recognition.

Next day Penelope told her son that he was now old enough to take charge of his own kingdom. She must give up her position as mistress of the palace and decide to choose one or the other of the suitors. In this way uncertainty would be ended; she would go off to the home of the winner, so that all the other suitors could be sent away, and peace and order would be restored in Ithaca under the rule of Telemachus. There would be a contest among the suitors for the honour of marrying her. A row of twelve axes was to be set up in the earth floor of the great hall. In the centre of each axe-head was a hole. Then the mighty bow of Odysseus was to be brought from the place where it had been stored for the past twenty years. Any man who wanted to enter the competition had first to string the bow, then fit an arrow to it and try to shoot it clean through the twelve holes. The first to succeed would be declared the winner.

Next day another feast was prepared, and the suitors came into the great hall and took their places. Once more, Odysseus, in the guise of a ragged beggar, sat at a small table beside the door. Once more he was given food and drink, and once more Antinous and some of the others began to mock at him, throwing him insults and meat bones. Telemachus told them angrily that they must not insult a stranger so long as *he* was master in his own house. He was now of age and was determined to see that the rules of courtesy were obeyed.

Some of the suitors told the young man that he was quite right to insist on his position as head of the house. But his mother, they said, must keep them waiting no longer and make up her mind which of them she was going to marry.

'We have been kept waiting too long already,' they said. 'She must know that Odysseus will never come back. Let her make up her mind this very day.'

'That she will do this very day,' answered Telemachus. 'She

may marry whom she pleases. I will not stop her.'

So when the feasting and drinking were done, Penelope herself, who had been with her servants in the women's quarters, appeared in front of the assembled suitors, bearing in her hands the great bow of Odysseus.

'All who will,' she said, 'may enter the contest for my hand. But the man who marries me must be as strong and valiant as my first husband was. Let each competitor take this bow and bend it. Then let him shoot an arrow at the mark which will now be set up. The strongest and straightest bowman shall be my rightful husband.'

Then Penelope withdrew from the hall, leaving the bow for the suitors to try. They gazed in awe at the mighty weapon which no man had strung for twenty years. The axes were set up in a row, all the blades pointing one way, and the holes at the centre of each axe-head exactly in line.

'Who is to be the first to try the bow of the mighty Odysseus?' demanded Telemachus.

A young man stepped forward, grasped the bow and tried to bend it. He failed and was followed by a second one and a third. None could even string the bow, much less aim an arrow through the axes. In the end only Antinous and another of the suitors, Eurymachus, were left. All considered them the strongest of the contestants.

Then Eumaeus and another shepherd, Philoetius, left the feast to go about their work. Odysseus stopped them outside the door of the hall and asked if they were both loyal to their former master. When they said they were, he told them who he was and asked if they were willing to help in the fight against the princes. Both agreed, and Odysseus told them to come back into the hall. There he would himself ask for the bow. The suitors would refuse, but Eumaeus and Philoetius were to give him the bow and then go to the women's quarters and tell them to make fast the doors at the back of the hall, so that no one could escape. Next they were to make fast the main doors.

Then Antinous raised his voice and cried.

'Let us all now go home, and tomorrow we will finish the contest. I and my rival Eurymachus will be fresher tomorrow, and we will try our strength.'

'Before you go, noble sirs,' said Odysseus quietly, 'let *me* try to bend the bow. I am a poor beggar and have no desire to ask for the hand of Penelope. But once I was sturdy and active, and I would like to see if I have lost all my former strength.'

Some laughed. All stared at the half-starved beggar in rage. Angrily they refused his request. But Telemachus insisted that the old man had a right to try, and Eumaeus took him the bow. While Odysseus was preparing to test his strength, Eumaeus and Philoetius disappeared quietly to do as they had been told, closing and barring all the doors that led from the great hall.

Odysseus then tried the bow and strung it with ease. All marvelled to see the beggar pluck the string and to hear it sing at his touch. Then he picked up an arrow, took aim and sent it hissing through the air. It passed clean through the holes in the line of axes. At this moment Zeus, father of all the gods, sent a sudden clap of thunder as a sign that the hour of Odysseus's vengeance had come. At the same moment the goddess Athene removed from Odysseus the semblance of a beggar and made him appear in his true form – that of a bronzed and handsome warrior in the full vigour of manhood. Seizing a second metal-tipped shaft, he aimed it at Antinous. It went clean through his throat, and Antinous groaned and fell dead on the floor, blood streaming from the wound.

Before the others could recover from their amazement, Odysseus, standing erect upon the threshold, raised his voice and spoke out in stern and terrifying accents.

'You who have rioted in my palace and laid waste my land – you who seek to carry off my true and lawful wife – know you that Odysseus has returned to his kingdom and that the hour of vengeance has come!'

Eurymachus, who was a coward at heart, began to whine for mercy. He claimed that Antinous, who was now dead, had led them all on. If only Odysseus would have mercy on them, they would depart, leaving him and his country in peace. For answer Odysseus told him they must all pay the full price of their riotous insolence. So Eurymachus told the other suitors they must draw their swords and fight for their lives. Instantly Odysseus fitted another arrow to the bow and shot Eurymachus dead.

Then Telemachus killed with his sword one of the suitors who was trying to flee. There was panic, and on discovering that they could not get out of the hall on account of the barred doors, the suitors determined to fight it out. There were many of them against Odysseus and his three loyal comrades – Telemachus, Eumaeus and Philoetius.

Things began to look black for them, when the goddess Athene appeared in the person of Mentor, an old companion whom Odysseus had left in charge of his household when he departed for Troy. Odysseus appealed to Mentor, who promised help and bade the hero to be of stout heart. Then the goddess flew off in the form of a swallow, to light on one of the rafters overhead. The battle went on. Telemachus and Eumaeus were wounded. Despite this, the courage and fury of the defenders, aided by the goddess, were redoubled. Panic seized the suitors, who tried vainly to escape. In the crush all were slain. Bloody but victorious, Odysseus and his comrades were in possession of the hall, the palace and the kingdom.

The delight of Penelope on being reunited with her husband can scarcely be imagined. It was Eurycleia, the old nurse, who broke the news of her husband's return and of his victory over the hated princes. Next day they went to tell the almost unbelievable story to Laertes, Odysseus's father. The old man could scarcely speak for joy and astonishment.

Thus Odysseus and his family were brought together again in peace and happiness after the trials of the Trojan war and the perilous adventures of the long voyage home.

Antoine de Saint-Exupéry
The Little Prince £4.99

The Little Prince comes to earth to learn the secret of what is really
important in life. He tells an air pilot in the Sahara Desert what he has
learned, in stories about the planet where he lives – stories about a haughty
flower, his fight with the bad seeds, and other planets and their rulers.

Rudyard Kipling
The Jungle Book £2.99

Full of unforgettable characters – Mowgli, the boy abandoned in the jungle
and raised by the Wolf Pack; Kaa, the Rock Python whose Dance
mesmerised even Baloo and Bagheera; Rikki-Tikki-Tavi, the brave
mongoose who fought and killed the big black cobra; and more . . .

The magical stories in *The Jungle Book* have enchanted generations since
they were first published nearly 100 years ago. Wonderful fairy tales, they
will be much appreciated when read aloud to young children.

Just So Stories £2.99

How the Elephant's Child has his nose pulled by the Crocodile; how the
Rhinoceros got his skin and a very bad temper; how the Leopard, in a spot,
took the Wise Bavarian's advice and got spots . . .

The *Just So Stories*, originally told to his daughter, are among Kipling's
finest. Witty and inventive, with illustrations full of hidden jokes and
puzzles by the author himself, they will be much appreciated when read
aloud to younger children.

All Pan books are available at your local bookshop or newsagent, or can be ordered direct from the publisher. Indicate the number of copies required and fill in the form below.

Send to: **CS Department, Pan Books Ltd., P.O. Box 40,**
             Basingstoke, Hants.   RG21 2YT.

or phone: 0256 469551 (Ansaphone), quoting title, author
             and Credit Card number.

Please enclose a remittance* to the value of the cover price plus: 60p for the first book plus 30p per copy for each additional book ordered to a maximum charge of £2.40 to cover postage and packing.

*Payment may be made in sterling by UK personal cheque, postal order, sterling draft or international money order, made payable to Pan Books Ltd.

Alternatively by Barclaycard/Access:

Card No.

Signature:

Applicable only in the UK and Republic of Ireland.

While every effort is made to keep prices low, it is sometimes necessary to increase prices at short notice. Pan Books reserve the right to show on covers and charge new retail prices which may differ from those advertised in the text or elsewhere.

NAME AND ADDRESS IN BLOCK LETTERS PLEASE:

....

Name————————————————————————————

Address————————————————————————————

————————————————————————————————

————————————————————————————————

————————————————————————————————

3/8